Name ____________ S0-AGV-050

Alphabetical Order

Luke is starting to become very interested in sports, but he is not sure which one he wants to try. He decided that he would first look up a good definition of some different sports before he decides.

Help Luke by putting these sports in alphabetical order the way he will find them in the dictionary. Then, pick out a sport that you are **unfamiliar** with and look it up and write its definition.

hockey	basketball
polo	archery
handball	rugby
curling	soccer
baseball	trapshooting
squash	fencing

1. ____________
2. ____________
3. ____________
4. ____________
5. ____________
6. ____________
7. ____________
8. ____________
9. ____________
10. ____________
11. ____________
12. ____________

Sport ____________ ____________________

____

____

Name ______________________

Introducing Guide Words

Luke is just learning to use the guide words in the dictionary and he needs lots of help. Help him decide on each of these entry words. Should he look on the page, turn forward, or turn back in the dictionary?

EXAMPLE: Guide Words | **Entry Word** | **Choices**

candy – cat | car | On Page-Turn Back-Turn Forward

Luke should circle On Page because **r** comes between **n** and **t** in the alphabet.

Circle the correct answers. Then, connect the circles you have made to discover Info's middle initial. **Clue:** Turn paper left!

Guide Words	Entry Word	Choices
hat – high	heel	On Page – Turn Back – Turn Forward
sat – save	sap	On Page – Turn Back – Turn Forward
ant – ape	area	On Page – Turn Back – Turn Forward
mars – mat	mask	On Page – Turn Back – Turn Forward
wind – won	wipe	On Page – Turn Back – Turn Forward
barn – basic	ball	On Page – Turn Back – Turn Forward
torn – tow	tower	On Page – Turn Back – Turn Forward
noon – now	nice	On Page – Turn Back – Turn Forward
girl – given	girth	On Page – Turn Back – Turn Forward

Name ______________________________

Reference Guide Words

Reference books have Guide Words at the top of each page. Luke and Info have found that these guide words are very important. The two words give you clues about what other words you will find on the page. Look at the dictionary pages below to explain these special clues.

The word on the left-hand side is always the first word on the page. The word on the right-hand side is the last word on the page.

Write five words that could be found on page 24 of the dictionary below. Circle the words at the bottom on the page that come between the Guide Words "ant" and "auto".
Write five words of your own that could be found on that page.

animal	after	action	arch	ambulance	art
ask	body	addition	attention	always	all	answer
apple	anteater	age	acre	awake	car

Name ____________________

More Guide Words

Look at each set of guide words. Write the words from the box at the bottom under the correct set of guide words. Four of the words will not fit. Put an **X** on those words.

ankle apple	cat cow	dash dog
________	________	________
________	________	________
________	________	________
________	________	________

fat forest	land little	man more
________	________	________
________	________	________
________	________	________
________	________	________

lap answer ape fist lent date center foam moreover
mile come ant fate dig chicken dark letter appear
men day danger cave list far manner felon moan do

Name ____________________

Guide Word Practice

Luke and info still need help with Guide Words. Look at the sample pages below. Write the entry words under the correct guide words. Do not forget to put them in alphabetical order.

Guide Words

brute   Buenos Aires

____
____
____
____
____
____
____
____
____
____

Guide Words

buff   bullish

____
____
____
____
____
____
____
____
____
____

Entry Words

bubble bud bulk build bucket bung budget
burr buck bug budge buckshot bullet bugle
bullion buffalo buccaneer buddy buckeye buffoon
bulletin bulb buoy

Circle the words that don't fit on these pages.

Name ____________________

More Practice

Library Luke and his two friends Info and Fiction Finch are having a contest. On the practice work below, they each think that their column will have the most items circled. Do the practice and then list the winner here. ____________

EXAMPLE:	Entry Word	Where to Look		
	Character	Front	Middle	Back

You should have circled the word **front** because **c** comes near the front of the alphabet, and therefore could be found at the front of the dictionary.

Entry Words	Where to Look		
baker	Front	Middle	Back
camel	Front	Middle	Back
window	Front	Middle	Back
bastion	Front	Middle	Back
yule	Front	Middle	Back
canyon	Front	Middle	Back
royal	Front	Middle	Back
zebra	Front	Middle	Back
kangaroo	Front	Middle	Back
nile	Front	Middle	Back
garage	Front	Middle	Back
downtown	Front	Middle	Back
lifeguard	Front	Middle	Back
anvil	Front	Middle	Back
bridge	Front	Middle	Back
elephant	Front	Middle	Back

Name ____________________________

Pronunciation

Sometimes when Luke is reading his library book, he comes across a word that he is not sure how to pronounce. He has learned to use his dictionary to figure out the way to pronounce it. To do this he must first use the **Pronunciation Key.**

Look carefully at the key. Each symbol above the vowels represents a certain sound. The example word for each sound is a small word that Luke already knows how to pronounce.

Now look at the key and put the key words next to the word that matches the pronunciation symbols.

Key				
ă – pat	ĭ – pit	ŭ – cut	o͞o – boot	ō – no
ā – pay	ī – pie	ū – pupil	ou – out	ô – for
ĕ – pet	ŏ – pot	ə - item	îr – pier	ē – be

prōrāt __________ __________

fôrm __________

bōt __________

sēj __________

krēp __________

ĕsā __________ __________

hăləbət __________ __________ __________

hăknē __________ __________

wălz __________

skāt __________

kădrē __________ __________

tîr __________

Write the correct spelling of each of the words written above.

__________ __________ __________ __________

__________ __________ __________ __________

__________ __________ __________ __________

Name______________________

Defining Words

Info has discovered that it is not always easy to find out the meanings of words in a dictionary. The other day he was having trouble figuring out what to do with his new toy. The directions said, "wind," and the meaning he looked at said, "air in motion". He is now all out of breath because he read the wrong definition for the word **wind**. He should have used the meaning that read, "to turn".

A word like **wind** is called a homograph because it has two different meanings.

Write two definitions for the homographs listed below:

stamp______________________

____

light ______________________

____

turn ______________________

____

mind ______________________

____

fall ______________________

____

read______________________

____

note______________________

____

pan ______________________

____

forge ______________________

____

bang ______________________

____

tap ______________________

____

wound ______________________

____

mean ______________________

____

lug______________________

____

Name ______________________________

More Defining

Luke has discovered that before a definition of a word is listed in a dictionary, an initial is listed to identify the part of speech. These are the initials used:

n – noun
v – verb
adj – adjective
adv – adverb
prep – preposition

Often the same word could be used as a noun, verb, adjective, adverb or preposition, depending on the context in which the word is used.

Read each sentence below, then look up the underlined word and write the part of speech that goes with the context.

1. He now works for a bankrupt company. ______
2. I will coast down the hill on my sled. ______
3. The parachute was torn. ______
4. Iron can be found in our state. ______
5. I ran forward. ______
6. The overdue bill will bankrupt him. ______
7. The coast was not far away. ______
8. He will parachute from the tower. ______
9. The iron gates were hard to open. ______
10. The forward compartment is full. ______
11. Light the fire to give light to the room. ______ ______
12. It is your turn to turn off the music. ______ ______
13. The nurse wound a bandage around the wound. ______ ______
14. Do you mind if I mind your little baby? ______ ______

Name ____________________

Origin of Words

Luke and Info discovered that often we get words from other languages. This is always noted in a dictionary. Here are some abbreviations to watch for.

Sp. – Spanish
Chin. – Chinese
Du. – Dutch
Ital. – Italian
Lat. – Latin
M.E. – Middle English
Turk. – Turkish
Fr. – French

Look up each word on Info's list and write its origin on the blank.

crêpe ______
veto ______
incognito ______
video ______
fiancée ______
judo ______
museum ______
governor ______
satellite ______
papaya ______
soprano ______
isthmus ______
grandiose ______
coffee ______
bastion ______
howitzer ______
hood ______
anchovy ______
bravo ______

Name ____________________

Looking for Base Words

Luke was playing baseball the other day and a friend told him that he was using an unofficial ball. Luke didn't understand, so he went to look it up in his dictionary. He looked under "uno-", but he could not find it.

When looking up words with prefixes, you need to identify the base word and look it up. Then add the meaning of the prefix to the definition. Here are some common prefixes and their meanings.

un – not, or opposite of
pre – before in time
mis – wrong, not
dis – not
de – do the opposite of

Examine the words below and circle the base word in each and then write the meanings.

1. misinterpret ____________________
2. unprecedented ____________________
3. disaffiliate ____________________
4. prehistoric ____________________
5. deactivate ____________________
6. uncomfortable ____________________
7. premeditated ____________________
8. misconception ____________________
9. disappointment ____________________
10. delineate ____________________

Name ____________________

Types of Books

There are three basic types of books that you can find in the library. My assistant Info has sniffed out some interesting facts about these three kinds of books.

FACTS: **Reference Books:** These are books that will be used in the library and not taken out. Reference books have facts and information about certain subject areas.

Fiction Books: These books are written in a make-believe way. The writer uses his imagination to write. These books are placed in alphabetical order by the last name of the writer.

Non-Fiction Books: These books have true stories and facts. Non-Fiction books are placed on the shelves using a special numbering system called the Dewey Decimal System.

Help Info put the correct letter next to the description of the books below. Put an **R** for reference book, **F** for fiction and **N** for non-fiction.

1. An Ewok adventure book with "Star Wars" creatures ___
2. A **B** encyclopedia that can't be taken from the library ___
3. An Almanac that can't be taken from the library ___
4. A book about the life of George Washington ___
5. A book about Superman ___
6. A science book that has a Dewey Decimal number on it ___
7. A book about Michael Jordan ___
8. The story of an airplane pilot that flew his airplane to the Moon ___
9. A book about a little boy that you would find on the shelf in a certain place because the writer's last name starts with the letter **B** ___
10. The story about the life of John F. Kennedy ___

Name ____________________

ABC Order by Name

Luke has learned that he needs to practice his **ABC** order skills. He knows that fiction books are placed in **ABC** order by the last name of the author. Look at the authors' names below and put them in the correct order by putting the right numbers in the blanks. The first one has already been done by Luke.

The Wizard of Oz by Frank Baum ____

Treasure Island by Robert Stevenson ____

Ramona the Brave by Beverly Cleary ____

West From Home by Laura Ingalls Wilder ____

The Borrowers by Mary Norton ____

The Tale of Peter Rabbit by Beatrix Potter ____

The Ugly Duckling by Hans Christian Andersen _1_

Where the Wild Things Are by Maurice Sendak ____

Alice in Wonderland by Lewis Carroll ____

The Incredible Journey by Sheila Burnford ____

A B C D E F G H I J K L M N O P Q R S T U V W X Y Z

Name ____________________

Card Catalog

Info has discovered that one way to find books in the library is to use the Card Catalog. In the Card Catalog you can find books listed in three different ways. They will be listed in the catalog by **Author, Title** and **Subject**. This means that there will be three cards for each book in the catalog.

Each drawer in the Card Catalog has guide letters on the front of the drawer to tell you what cards will be in the drawer.

Look at the drawer that Info is using. Circle the books that will have cards for them in this drawer.

Titles

Child of the Owl by Albers
Autumn Poetry by Coliton
Africa by Tally
Chinese Poetry by Tai
All About Snakes by Simpson
The Talking Tree by Baker
Fairy Tales by Andersen
Anasi, the Spider Man by Sherlock
Miss Hickory by Bailey
Winnie the Pooh by Milne
Strawberry Girl by Linski
The Wind and the Willows by Grahame
Learn About Birds by Goldman

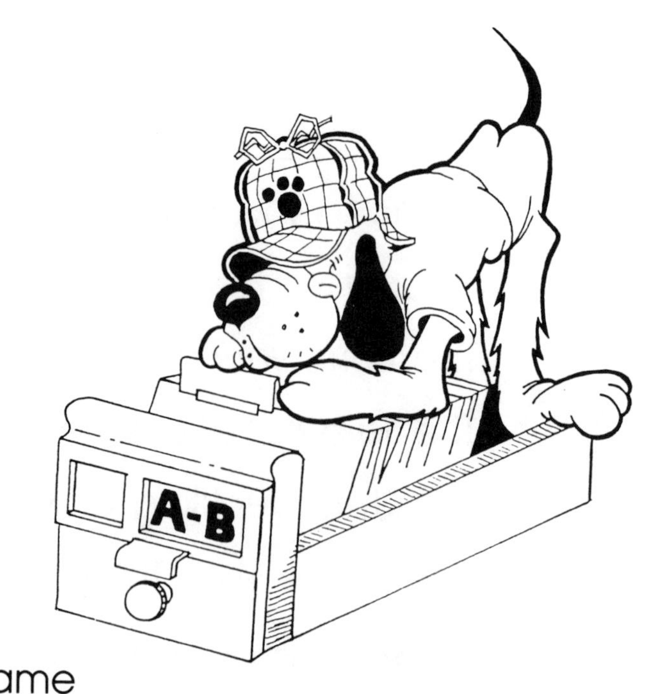

On the back of the paper, list five more titles that **could be** found in this drawer. Use your imagination and make them up!

More Card Catalog

Name ____________________

Luke and Info often use encyclopedias to do their reports. Sometimes they need more specific information on a subject. When this is so, they go to the Card Catalog. The Card Catalog consists of drawers with cards that list every book on the library shelves. As a matter of fact, each book in the library has three cards in the catalog: one card in alphabetical order by the author's last name, one in order by the title and one by the subject. Here is an example:

752.8 Painting – Watercolor
Allen, Fred
Watercolor Painting
by Fred Allen
Judy Publishing Co.
986

752.8 Allen, Fred
All **Watercolor Painting**
Judy Publishing Co.
105 P

752.8 Watercolor Painting
All Allen, Fred
Watercolor Painting by
Fred Allen
Judy Publishing Co.

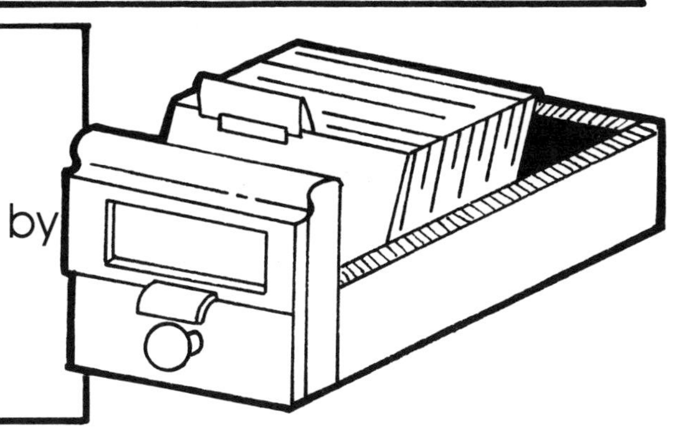

Go to the Card Catalog and see how many books have cards with the subject of:

Oil Painting ________ Ballerinas ________ Peace Corps ________

Mother Teresa ________ Vitamin C ________ Schooners ________

Weight Lifting ________ Harness Racing ________ Navajo Indians ________

Sanskrit ________ Bauxite ________ John F. Kennedy ________

Dirigibles ________ Christopher Columbus ________

Name ______________________________

Card Catalog Review

Let's take a good look at one of these make-believe cards from a Card Catalog and let Luke explain it to you.

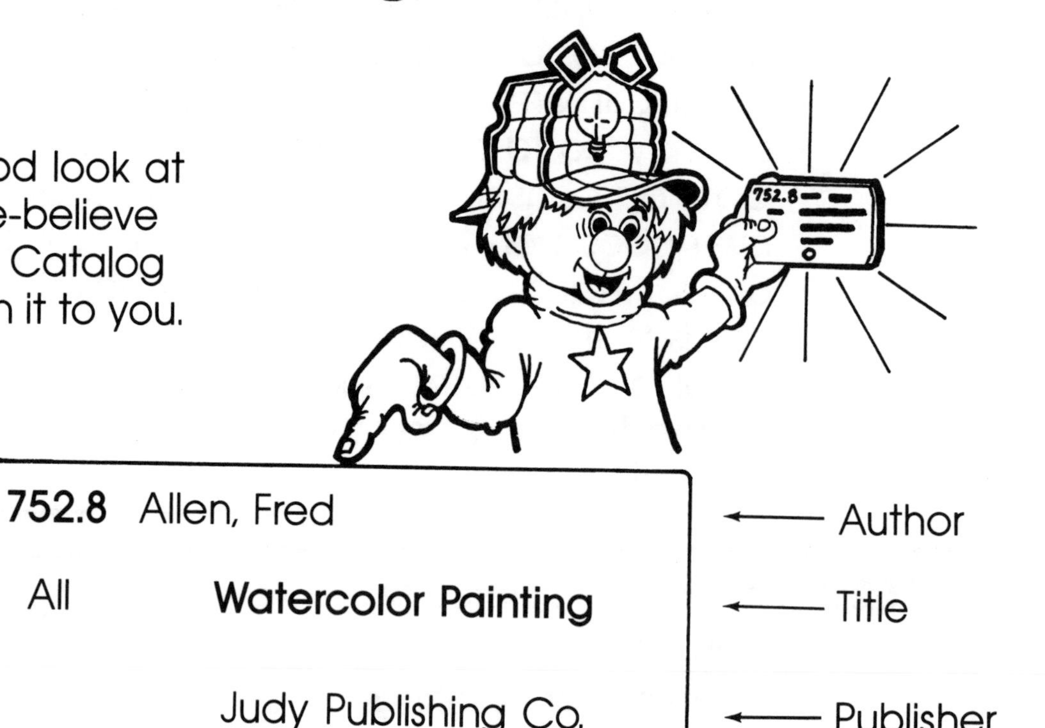

Call Numbers → | 752.8 Allen, Fred | ← Author

All **Watercolor Painting** ← Title

Judy Publishing Co. ← Publisher

105 p ← Pages

Fill in the blanks:

Library books will have __________ cards in the Card Catalog. These cards are categorized by______________ , ______________ and ______________ in alphabetical order.

______________ is the name of the company that made this book. There are ______ pages in this book. __________ is the last name of the author. The ______________ number in the upper left corner of this card is ______________ and it helps you find the book on the ______________ .

Go to the Card Catalog and find three cards for the author Laura Ingles Wilder. List the call numbers.

__________ __________ __________

Name ____________________

Almanac

Another reference book that Luke and Info have learned to appreciate is the **Almanac**. This is a book that contains lots of different kinds of facts and information. The facts and information is always very current because it is published each year.

The information is not listed in alphabetical order, so therefore you must always look in the index to find which page you need.

THE KNOW-IT-ALL-MANAC

Use an Almanac to find the information called for below.

1. What is the current population of your state? ____________________
2. In 1984, what were two important stories in the news? ____________________
   ____
3. What is the governor's name in Colorado? ____________________
4. What does Colorado mean? ____________________
5. Who won the Super Bowl this year? ____________________
6. What motion picture won the Academy Award for best picture in 1984? ____________________
7. Who are two people in the Baseball Hall of Fame? ____________________
   ____
8. Who was Miss America in 1980? ____________________
9. What is the longest-running Broadway play ever? ____________________
   ____
10. Who ran for U.S. President as an Independent in the 1980 election?
    ____

LOOK IT UP

List four interesting facts that you find in the 1992 almanac.

____________________ ____________________

____________________ ____________________

Name ______________________________

Almanac Research

Do this math problem to come up with your "Year to Remember". Next, find the Almanac for that year and fill in the information below.

Math Problem:

Take the year you were born and add ten years. Substract three years and that is your "Year to Remember". ____________

A Year to Remember

Sports

Who won the World Series? ______________________________

Who won the Super Bowl? ______________________________

Government

Who was the President? ______________________________

Who was Governor of your state? ______________________________

Entertainment

What was voted best movie? ______________________________

What was the TV program of the year? ______________________________

Name the top two news stories ______________________________

Vital Statistics

How many births in the U.S. in that year? ______________________________

How many deaths? ______________________________

On the back of your paper, add one more category to the list and write two questions about it.

Name ____________________

More Almanac Research

Library Luke and Info are doing some research about the year 1977. That is the year that Luke was born. Help with the research and answer the questions below by looking in an Almanac. Find the correct pages by looking in the index.

Disasters that happened in 1977 are categorized into several categories, such as: Assassinations, Blizzards, Earthquakes, Floods, etc.

Where did a flood occur in 1977? ____________________

What type of airline crashed in Indiana? ____________________

Arts and Media is a category that Luke finds entertaining.

Who was Miss America in 1977? ____________________

In January 1977, what television movie was an all-time television program viewed by many people? ____________________

Sports are always exciting to Luke!

What horse won the Kentucky Derby in 1977? ____________________

What basketball team won the N.B.A.? ____________________

Being a detective, Luke is curious about crime.

How many murders were committed in 1977? ____________________

What percent of households were touched by crime that year? ____________

Look up the category "Congress of the United States". Write two questions about it relating to 1977.

Name ______________________

Atlas

Library Luke and Info have found another important research tool. It is called an Atlas. An Atlas is a book of maps.

Luke's parents are taking him on vacation soon. He promised his dad that he would learn to read a map so that he could help with directions.

They are going to Springfield, Illinois. On the map next to the name of the city, he found the code **H-5**. The **H** represents the letters along the side of the map. The number represents the numbers along the bottom of the map. This helps you find things on the map more easily.

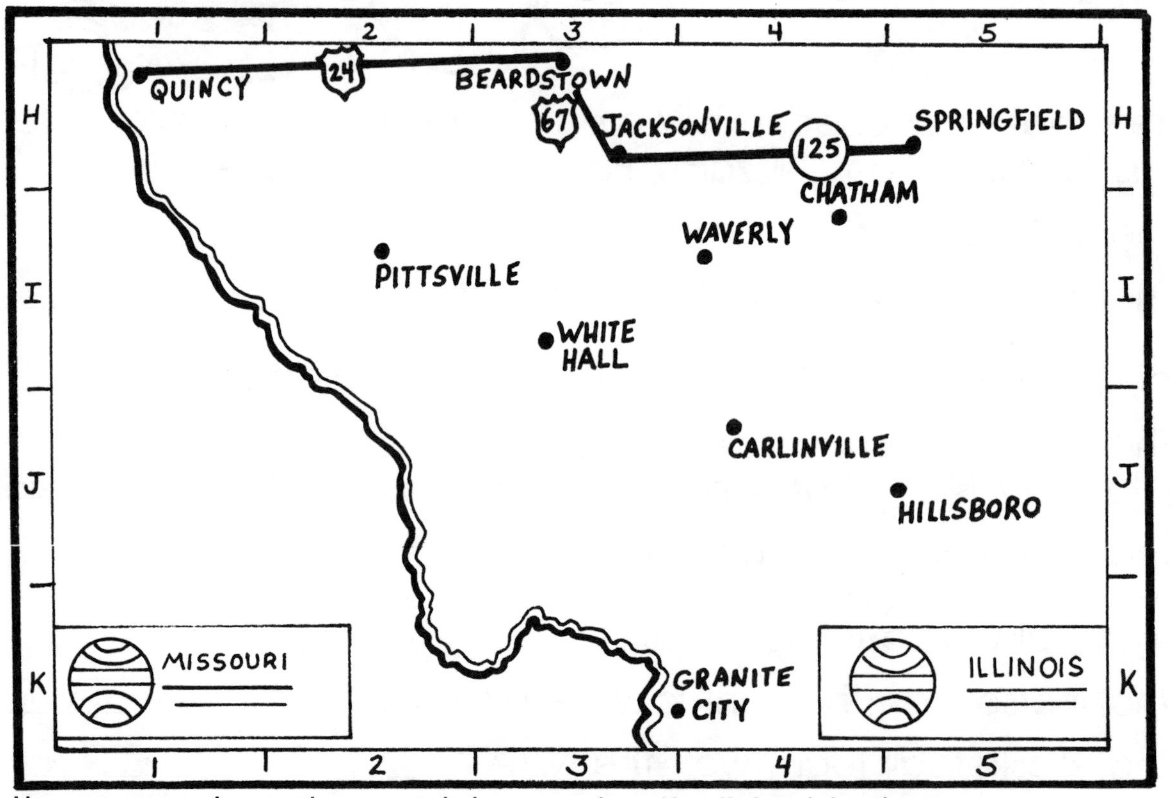

Write the correct codes next to each city listed below.

Jacksonville ______ Carlinville ______ Pittsville ______

Beardstown ______ Quincy ______ Chatham ______

White Hall ______ Waverly ______ Granite City ______

Hillsboro ______

Library Luke lives in Quincy. What highway(s) would he take to get to Springfield? ______________________

Name ______________________________

Introduction to Dewey Decimal

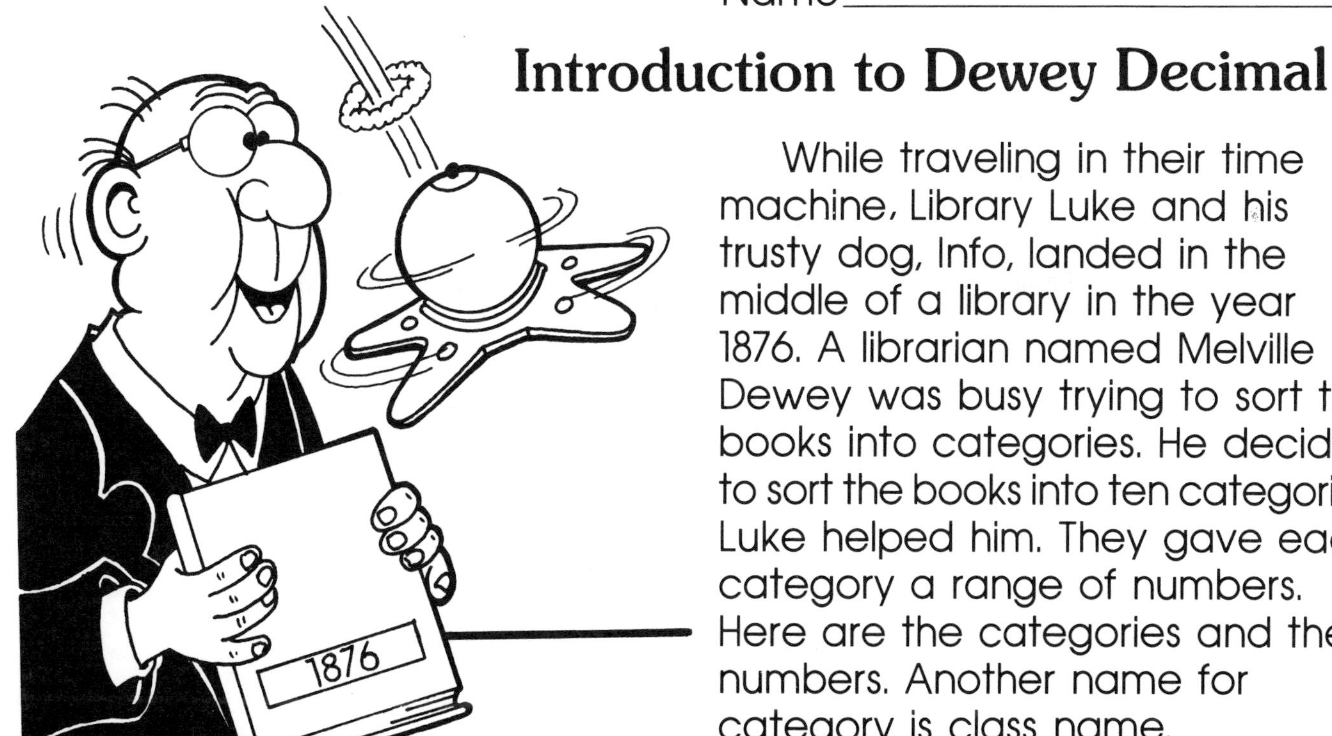

While traveling in their time machine, Library Luke and his trusty dog, Info, landed in the middle of a library in the year 1876. A librarian named Melville Dewey was busy trying to sort the books into categories. He decided to sort the books into ten categories. Luke helped him. They gave each category a range of numbers. Here are the categories and their numbers. Another name for category is class name.

Categories	Numbers	List one book for each.
Generalities	000-099	______________
Philosophy	100-199	______________
Religion	200-299	______________
The Social Sciences	300-399	______________
Language	400-499	______________
Pure Sciences	500-599	______________
Technology	600-699	______________
The Arts	700-799	______________
Literature	800-899	______________
Geography and History	900-999	______________

Unscramble these words to discover the name of the system Mr. Dewey invented.

EWYED MALDECI MESYTS

____

Name ______________________________

Generalities

The first category, **Generalities,** includes encyclopedias, bibliographies, periodicals and journalism books. These books have numbers from **000** to **099.**

Luke is helping Dewey put the numbers on the spines of these books. As the books are numbered, they are then put on the shelves in the library. Go to your library and find these books on the shelves. Write step-by-step directions on how someone would find these books in your library. Below you will find directions that Luke wrote.

EXAMPLE: When entering the library from the east door, turn toward the windows and find the brown shelves. While facing the shelves, the books in the **Generalities** category will be on the shelves closest to the windows.

Luke wants to hear your directions on how to find the **Generalities** in your library.

____

____

____

____

____

____

____

Name ______________________________

Philosophy

Philosophy is the study of thinking. Some of the first people to really practice philosophy were from ancient Greece. One of the most noted of these ancient Greek philosophers was Plato. Since the study of philosophy started so long ago, Dewey started numbering his system with this being his first subject.

Since this is the first subject in Dewey's categories, Luke remembers the numbers because they start at **100** and go to **199.**

Fill in the blanks.

Since ________________ is the study of thinking, Plato would be called a ________________. Since this type of study was one of the first subjects studied back in ancient ____________, Mr. Dewey numbered books in this category from ______ to ______.

Now go to the library and find five books from this category.

____

____

____

____

____

Write a trivia question about an ancient philosopher. Try to stump your classmates.____

____

Name ______________________________

Religion

A man by the name of Johannes Gutenberg invented the first printing press back in the 15th century. One of the first books that Gutenberg printed was a Bible. Mr. Dewey chose the Bible and other religious books to fill the next category.

Library Luke and Info are starting to understand the Dewey Decimal System. The first category of books is **Generalities** which has no certain subjects. Then the first formal subject studied was **Philosophy,** so that is Dewey's second category. Next, books about **Religion** fill the third category because they were the first books in print.

Fill in the blanks below and circle your answers in the word search.

Books about the study of thinking are ________________ books.

Melville ______________ put the books into categories.

__________________________ invented a printing press to print Bibles.

Religious books fit into the ______________ category.

In Dewey's categories, non-______________ books have certain numbers.

Books numbered **200** to **299** are books about ________________.

S	R	F	C	G	T	K	O	S	C	W	A	D
D	E	R	T	Y	O	P	K	J	A	W	D	E
A	T	T	H	I	R	D	E	Q	X	P	L	W
T	M	U	D	A	F	H	T	R	E	W	Q	E
P	H	I	L	O	S	O	P	H	Y	B	V	Y
J	I	S	D	R	E	L	I	G	I	O	N	K
K	O	P	D	G	U	T	E	N	B	E	R	G
F	I	C	T	I	O	N	H	R	W	D	F	U

Name____________________________

The Social Sciences

Luke is trying to explain to Info about the laws of our country. To read about laws and politics and customs, Luke needs to look at books which are numbered from **300** to **399**. Luke figured that Dewey put this category next because after religion the next things to be written down in books were laws. This category is called **Social Sciences**.

Circle the books from the **Social Sciences**' category. Then see how many of these you can find in your library.

From Gold to Money - 332.4
United Nations - 341.23
Warships - 359.8
Children of the Wild West - 305.2
Noah and the Ark – 222
Let's Talk about Fighting - 173
Thanksgiving - 394.2
Holidays - 394.203
Pinatas and Paper Flowers - 394.2

Choose one of the books you found and write three interesting facts from it.

____

____

____

____

____

Name_______________

Language

"Adios amigos!" said Luke. Info didn't understand him. Luke has been reading a Spanish book from the next category of Dewey's system.

The **Language** category contains books about foreign languages as well as our own English language. These books are numbered **400** to **499**.

Write the class name and class number for each of the titles below.

	Class Name	Class Number
St. Francis of Assissi	________	________
The Kid's Book About Death and Dying	________	________
Best-Loved Bible Verses for Children	________	________
Canada's Kids	________	________
The Unions	________	________
Christmas Time	________	________
The Story of the Erie Canal	________	________
Words to Talk About	________	________
Language	________	________

Name ____________________

Pure Sciences

To know what to look for with his new telescope, Luke needs to look in an astronomy book. This kind of book will be in Dewey's next category of books. The **Pure Sciences** category will contain books about math, biology, chemistry and all the pure sciences. These books will be numbered from **500** to **599**.

Luke went to the library to find books on astronomy. These are the directions he gave on how he found the books on astronomy.

EXAMPLE: I entered the library and found the shelves of non-fiction books near the north wall. The books numbered **500** to **599** were on the bottom shelf on the left. There I found four astronomy books.

Go to the library and find three books on astronomy and list their numbers below. Also, write a short description of where to find the Pure Sciences books like Luke did.

____

____

____

____

____

____

____

Name ____________________

Technology

Luke probably would not find a cure for Info's injured paw in medical books without having some sort of formal veterinarian training.

If Luke were going to study to be a veterinarian, he would be using books from Dewey's category of **Technology**.

These books are numbered in Dewey's system from **600** to **699**.

Go to the library. List the call numbers and titles for the subjects in each sentence.

	Call Numbers
1. Find two books about medical professions.	
____________________	________
____________________	________
2. Find two books about machines.	
____________________	________
____________________	________
3. Find three books about vehicles.	
____________________	________
____________________	________
____________________	________
4. Find two books about farming.	
____________________	________
____________________	________
5. Find two books about pets.	
____________________	________
____________________	________

Name ______________________

The Arts

Van Gogh, Picasso, El Greco and Raphael are all famous painters. To find out when they painted, Luke must look in the section of books that deal with the **Arts.** This category is numbered from **700** to **799**.

When looking, Luke found that the Dewey Decimal System is subdivided into smaller subject categories. These categories are listed at the right.

700	The Arts
710	Civic and Landscape Art
720	Architecture
730	Plastic Arts/Sculpture
740	Drawing, Decorative and Minor Arts
750	Painting & Paints
760	Graphic Arts/Prints
770	Photography and Photographs
780	Music
790	Recreational and Performing Arts

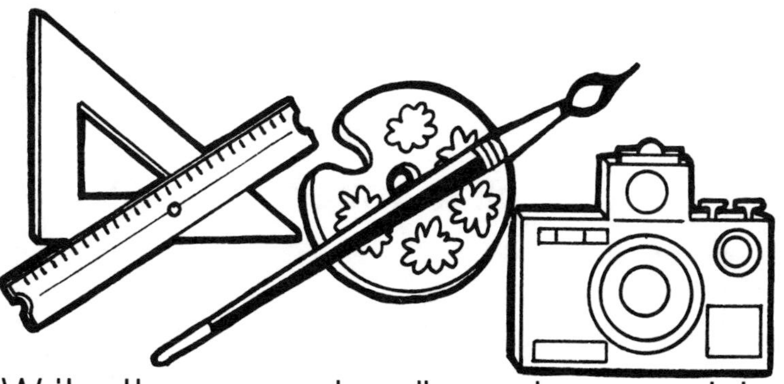

Write the correct call numbers next to their titles.

Pitching ______

Making Dolls ______

Famous Painting ______

The Art of Africa ______

Skyscrapers ______

Sketchbook ______

Creating with Clay ______

Roller Skating Is for Me ______

Make Mine Music! ______

Teenage Dance Book ______

Paper, Ink and Roller ______

Clay, Wood, and Wire ______

City: A Story of Roman Planning ______

What Makes an Orchestra ______

796	781	793	745	759	783	796
760	709	730	711	721	731	741

Name ______________________________

Literature

Literature means writings of verse or prose that have permanent value. Nursery rhymes that Luke reads to Info at bedtime can be found in this category of Dewey's system. Riddles and joke books are also found here. These books are all numbered from **800** to **899**.

Find a riddle book in this section. List the title and call number of the riddle book.

____
Title

____
Call Number

Copy two of your favorite riddles from the riddle book.

1. ______________________________

____

2. ______________________________

____

List the titles and call numbers of four interesting books in the literature section of your library.

1. ______________________________
2. ______________________________
3. ______________________________
4. ______________________________

Name ______________________________

Geography and History

Who wrote the Declaration of Independence? When did Alaska become a state? What countries fought in World War I? How big is the state of Georgia? What is the smallest continent on Earth? Who was Prime Minister of England in 1920? What is the longest river in Europe? What is the smallest state in the U.S.? All of these questions can be answered if you look in the right books. All of these questions concern **Geography** or **History**. Dewey put these kinds of books together in a category numbered **900** to **999**.

Find the answers to the questions above by looking in books from the **Geography/History** section. List the call numbers of the books where you found the answers.

	Answers	Call Numbers
1.	______________________	__________
2.	______________________	__________
3.	______________________	__________
4.	______________________	__________
5.	______________________	__________
6.	______________________	__________
7.	______________________	__________
8.	______________________	__________

Name ____________________

Research

When doing research it is important to know where to find the books you need. That is why it is helpful to know the Dewey Decimal System.

EXAMPLE: If Luke has a report to do on the Revolutionary War, he could look at books in two basic categories. He could look at books numbered **900** to **999** for History, and **300** to **399** for Social Science.

Below Luke has a list of reports that he has to complete. Next to each topic write the category he should look in for the information he needs.

Topics	Categories
American Generals	____________
Pets of the Presidents	____________
The First Veterinarian	____________
Poetry About Sports	____________
The First Printing Press	____________
Paintings of Presidents	____________
The History of Space Travel	____________
Architecture of Ancient Greece	____________
Cooking in Columbia	____________
The Religious Belief of the American Indian	____________

Name ______________________

Pure Sciences vs. Social Sciences

Write the book titles below under the proper categories.

Pure Sciences	Social Sciences
______________________	______________________
______________________	______________________
______________________	______________________
______________________	______________________
______________________	______________________

The KBG - 327.1
Deserts - 574.5
Submarines - 359.3
Little Giants - 591
Water - 533.95
Forests - 574.5
The Emergency Room - 362.1
Baby Dinosaurs - 567.9
First Class - 383
Rattlesnakes - 597.96

Now pick one of the books above and list it and at least seven others that could be read if writing a report on the topic.

1. ______________________
2. ______________________
3. ______________________
4. ______________________
5. ______________________
6. ______________________
7. ______________________
8. ______________________

Name______________________________

Zoological Science Activity

590	Zoological Sciences
591	Zoology
592	Invertebrates
593	Protozoa
594	Mollusks and Related Other Invertebrates
595	Insects
596	Chordates/Vetebrates
597	Cold-blooded Vertebrates
598	Birds
599	Mammals

Info is interested in learning more about science. He is especially interested in the zoological sciences because that is his category. He discovered that not only is each category subdivided, but so is each sub-category!

590 is the subdivision called **Zoological Sciences.** Information on Info would be in a book numbered **599** (Mammals).

Here is a challenge! See if you can number the book titles below. You may have to do some research!

The Crow Family ______

The Skeleton Book ______

Tiger of the Sea ______

The Story of Flies ______

Alligator ______

Bats ______

Gorilla Mysteries ______

Hyena Day ______

Ants and Termites ______

Zoos in the Making ______

The Knight in Crusty Armor______

The Book of Snakes ______

Peeper, First Voice of Spring ______

My Dear Dolphin ______

Animals Without Backbones ______

Experiments With Microscopic Animals ______

Name ______________________________

Introduction to Encyclopedias

Luke is climbing into an encyclopedia. If you have never climbed into one, Luke would like to invite you to climb into one soon.

An encyclopedia is set up in alphabetical order just like a dictionary. Anytime you have a question about anything, the encyclopedia is one of the first places you can look for an answer.

One of the neat things about encyclopedias is that if you look something up, you usually find out information that will lead you to look for something else in the encyclopedia.

Luke is going to look up airplanes in the **A** encyclopedia. When he looks it up, he will discover that the first airplane was invented by the Wright brothers. Can you guess which encyclopedia Luke will look in next to learn more about the Wright brothers?

Circle the correct encyclopedia.

List the encyclopedia you will need to answer these questions.

1. When did man first land on the moon? ___
2. When was George Washington born? ___
3. Who is Governor of Arizona? ___
4. What is a baseball made of? ___
5. How big is a football field? ___
6. Where is Mt. Everest? ___
7. Who lived at Monticello? ___
8. Who invented the car? ___

Name ______________________

Encyclopedias

After learning about dogs, Luke and Info decided to look up information about other animals in the encyclopedias. They decided to look up **fish**. Which encyclopedia do you think they should look in?

____

Look up fish in your encyclopedia and answer the questions below.

1. Do fish have backbones? ______
2. Where would you find the smallest fish swimming? ______________
3. What is the largest fish in the ocean? ______________
4. Name a fish that can fly. ______________
5. How do fish breathe under water? ______________
6. How long are seahorses? ______________
7. What is the name of the fin on the side of a fish? ______________
8. When did the first fish appear on the earth? ______________
9. Name a fish that you find unusual looking. ______________
10. Name a fish with more than two colors. ______________

This is enough information to write a report on fish. Write one using these facts. But don't just copy out of the encyclopedia!

Name ______________________________

People in Encyclopedias

When Luke wants to find information about famous people, he often looks in the encyclopedia first. Especially when he is doing a report about a famous person. He usually wants to know when the person was born.

At the beginning of an article about a famous person, you will find something that looks like this: (1952-1978). The first date in parenthesis, 1952, tells when the person was born. The second date refers to when the person died. Luke's would look like this if he were in the encyclopedia: (1977 -   ). This means that Luke was born in 1977, but that he has not died yet.

Go to the library and find the articles about these famous people. Fill in the correct dates in parenthesis for each individual.

John F. Kennedy	( )	Ian Fleming	( )
Thomas Edison	( )	Gertrude Ederle	( )
Jackie Robinson	( )	Walt Disney	( )
Ronald Reagan	( )	William Bonney	( )
Judy Garland	( )	Patrick Henry	( )
Susan B. Anthony	( )	Herbert Hoover	( )
Daniel Boone	( )	W. C. Fields	( )
Mary Bethune	( )	Eli Whitney	( )
Elizabeth Browning	( )	Babe Ruth	( )
Abe Lincoln	( )	Humphrey Bogart	( )

Write a short paragraph about one of these famous people.

Name ______________________________

Places in Encyclopedias

Info is planning his vacation and he is not sure where he is going to go. Luke told him to look in the encyclopedia to find some interesting places to visit. He knows he wants to see the capital in each state he visits. Also he wants to visit two interesting sites in each state. Look up each state and then list the capital and two interesting sites.

	Capital	Interesting Sites	
Missouri	____________	____________	____________
Colorado	____________	____________	____________
Illinois	____________	____________	____________
Vermont	____________	____________	____________
Texas	____________	____________	____________
Montana	____________	____________	____________
Tennessee	____________	____________	____________

On the back of this paper, write a short paragraph about an interesting site in your state.

Name ______________________________

Encyclopedia Wordsearch

To find the correct words in the Wordsearch, Luke must first do some research and answer the questions. First, decide which book you will look in to find the answer and write the letter of the encyclopedia in the blank space. Next, go to the library and find the answer. Next, circle the correct words in the Wordsearch.

1. What is the capital of Georgia? ___
2. Who was the fourth President of the U.S? ___
3. Who invented the telephone? ___
4. Where was Henry Ford born? ___
5. What do gray whales eat? ___
6. Where is brown coal found in the U.S.? ___
7. Who was president after Lincoln? ___
8. What did Clara Barton start? ___

R	E	D	C	R	O	S	S	L	P	K	P	P	L	A	N	K	T	O	N
K	G	F	I	N	E	R	Y	B	M	N	W	O	P	A	Z	Q	F	Y	M
A	T	L	A	N	T	A	F	R	E	W	X	C	V	Y	H	B	E	L	L
M	I	C	H	I	G	A	N	J	L	P	O	T	R	A	E	F	Y	U	B
N	J	M	A	D	I	S	O	N	J	O	H	N	S	O	N	K	Y	T	I
F	R	S	G	B	U	C	N	M	O	N	T	A	N	A	L	H	T	E	W

Write five questions that could be answered by looking in one encyclopedia. Exchange questions with a classmate.

Name ____________________

Encyclopedia Dot-to-Dot

To discover how Luke plans to send Info on a tour of Belgium, you must complete the dot-to-dot. As you answer each question, connect the dots that go with each starred letter. Connect the last dot to the first dot to complete the picture.

1. What is a language spoken in Belgium? ___ ___ ___ ___ ___*
2. What is the capital city? ___ ___ ___ ___ ___* ___ ___ ___
3. What is the highest mountain there? ___ ___ ___* ___ ___ ___ ___ ___ ___ ___
4. What is their main grain product? ___ ___* ___ ___ ___ ___
5. What continent is it on? ___ ___ ___ ___ ___ ___*
6. What U.S. state is the same size? ___ ___ ___ ___* ___ ___ ___ ___
7. What country is north of Belgium? ___ ___ ___ ___ ___ ___ ___ ___ ___ ___* ___
8. What religion are most of the people? ___ ___ ___* ___ ___ ___ ___ ___
9. What country is south of Belgium? ___ ___ ___ ___ ___* ___
10. What is the largest city in Belgium? ___ ___ ___ ___* ___ ___ ___
11. Who is head of their government? ___* ___ ___ ___ ___

    ___ ___ ___ ___ ___ ___ ___ ___
12. Who is Head of State? ___ ___* ___ ___

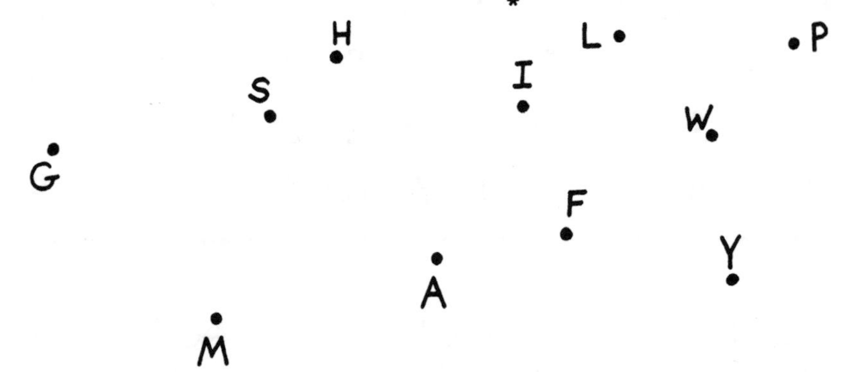

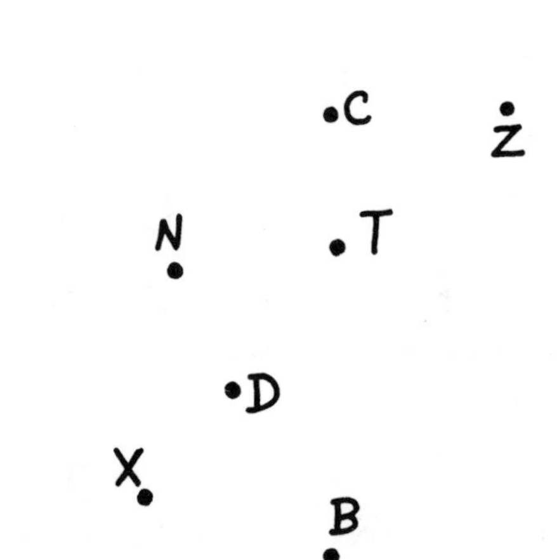

Name______________________

Encyclopedia Research

DOWN

1. Andrew Jackson died in what city?
2. What is the capital of the state where Abe Lincoln was born?
3. The president who followed Lincoln was born in what city?

ACROSS

4. What is the main agricultural product in Kansas?
5. What is the state bird of Lincoln's birthplace?
6. What river is near President Franklin Roosevelt's birthplace?
7. Thomas Jefferson was born in what state?
8. What president followed Theodore Roosevelt?
9. What state became a state when Theodore Roosevelt was in office?
10. What is the smallest state in the U.S.?

Name ________________________________

Library Review

Poor Info is so tired. He is ready to rest and let you use the information you have learned about libraries to fill in these answers.

Use these words to fill in the blanks.

fiction **card catalog** **non-fiction** **Dewey** **almanac**

1. A ______________ has books listed three different ways.
2. An ______________ is published every year and contains many different facts and information.
3. Books that are true are called ______________ .
4. ______________ was a librarian who invented a system of placing books in order in a library.
5. A book that is make-believe is called ______________ .

Now write a **T** if the sentence is true and **F** if it is false.

6. Fiction books are put in alphabetical order by their author's last name. ___
7. There are three kinds of books with Dewey Decimal numbers. ___
8. Reference books are untrue. ___
9. To find out about current things, look in an Almanac. ___
10. We usually keep reference books in the library. ___

Crossword Puzzle Fun

Across

1. Use a whisper voice in the ______________ .
3. Where to find current population.
5. Opposite of fiction.

Down

2. You can find maps where?
4. Another word for writer is?

Name ____________________

Reference Review

Info made a terrible mistake. His paw accidently hit the board where Luke was doing his homework and got the answers to the questions all scrambled up. Your job is to unscramble the words and put the correct answers on the lines.

recurtn	exind	iLnolnc	eddi	raesherc
protser	lasat	olctaag	revorgon	lamacan

1. In the encyclopedia, you can find out when a famous person was born and __________.
2. If you look up a state in the encyclopedia, you can discover the head of the government, the __________.
3. The __________ is where all the subjects in an Almanac are listed by page numbers.
4. Encyclopedias are very helpful when doing __________.
5. To find out about Abe Lincoln's life, you should look up __________.
6. __________ events can be found in a yearly Almanac.
7. The __________ will be subjects listed in the index by page number.
8. To find all the books in a library on a certain subject, you can look in the Card __________.
9. Maps of many places will be found in an __________.
10. When information is gathered for a report, we call it __________.

LOOK IT UP

Write five facts about Lincoln that you find interesting. Use at least two different reference books. List your sources.

Answer Key

Library and Reference Skills

Grades 4 - 5

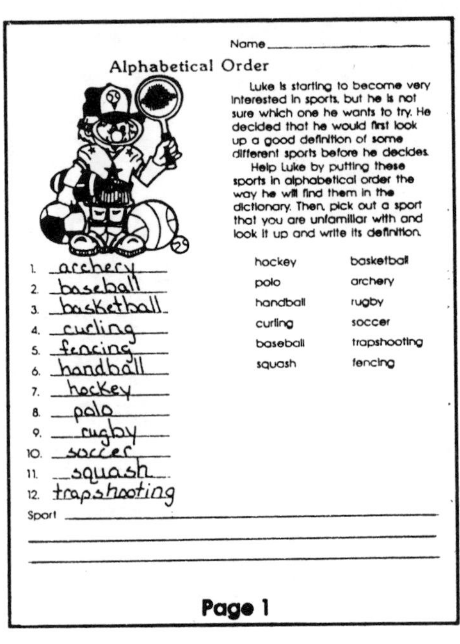

Name ____________

Alphabetical Order

Luke is starting to become very interested in sports, but he is not sure which one he wants to try. He decided that he would first look up a good definition of some different sports before he decides.

Help Luke by putting these sports in alphabetical order the way he will find them in the dictionary. Then, pick out a sport that you are unfamiliar with and look it up and write its definition.

hockey	basketball
polo	archery
handball	rugby
curling	soccer
baseball	trapshooting
squash	fencing

1. archery
2. baseball
3. basketball
4. curling
5. fencing
6. handball
7. hockey
8. polo
9. rugby
10. soccer
11. squash
12. trapshooting

Sport ____________

Page 1

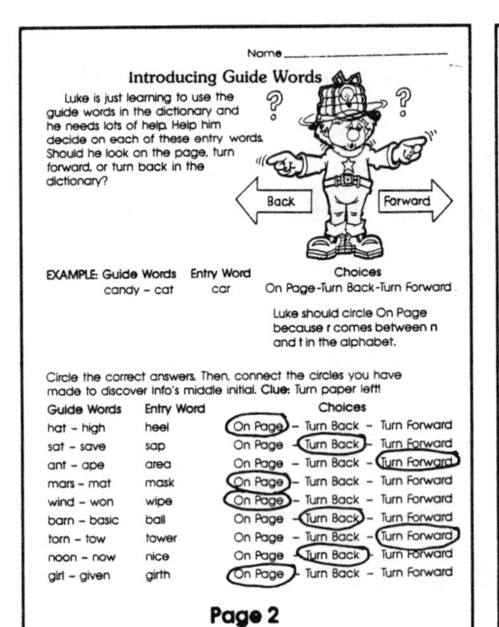

Name ____________

Introducing Guide Words

Luke is just learning to use the guide words in the dictionary and he needs lots of help. Help him decide on each of these entry words. Should he look on the page, turn forward, or turn back in the dictionary?

EXAMPLE: Guide Words: candy - cat; Entry Word: car; Choices: On Page-Turn Back-Turn Forward

Luke should circle On Page because r comes between n and t in the alphabet.

Circle the correct answers. Then, connect the circles you have made to discover Info's middle initial. **Clue:** Turn paper left!

Guide Words	Entry Word	Choices
hat - high	heel	(On Page) - Turn Back - Turn Forward
sat - save	sap	On Page - (Turn Back) - Turn Forward
ant - ape	area	On Page - Turn Back - (Turn Forward)
mars - mat	mask	(On Page) - Turn Back - Turn Forward
wind - won	wipe	(On Page) - Turn Back - Turn Forward
barn - basic	ball	On Page - (Turn Back) - Turn Forward
torn - tow	tower	On Page - Turn Back - (Turn Forward)
noon - now	nice	On Page - (Turn Back) - Turn Forward
girl - given	girth	(On Page) - Turn Back - Turn Forward

Page 2

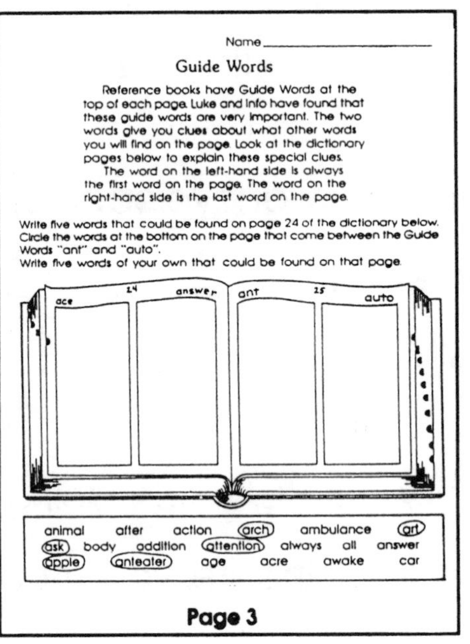

Name ____________

Guide Words

Reference books have Guide Words at the top of each page. Luke and Info have found that these guide words are very important. The two words give you clues about what other words you will find on the page. Look at the dictionary pages below to explain these special clues.

The word on the left-hand side is always the first word on the page. The word on the right-hand side is the last word on the page.

Write five words that could be found on page 24 of the dictionary below. Circle the words at the bottom on the page that come between the Guide Words "ant" and "auto".

Write five words of your own that could be found on that page.

animal after action (arch) ambulance (art) (ask) body addition (attention) always all answer (apple) (anteater) age acre awake car

Page 3

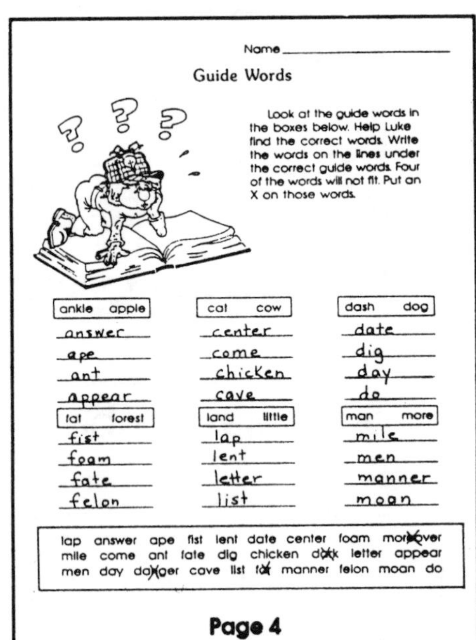

Name ____________

Guide Words

Look at the guide words in the boxes below. Help Luke find the correct words. Write the words on the lines under the correct guide words. Four of the words will not fit. Put an X on those words.

ankle apple	cat cow	dash dog
answer	center	date
ape	come	dig
ant	chicken	day
appear	cave	do

fat forest	land little	man more
fist	lap	mile
foam	lent	men
fate	letter	manner
felon	list	moan

lap answer ape fist lent date center foam mor~~ver~~ mile come ant fate dig chicken d~~u~~k letter appear men day da~~n~~ger cave list f~~o~~t manner felon moan do

Page 4

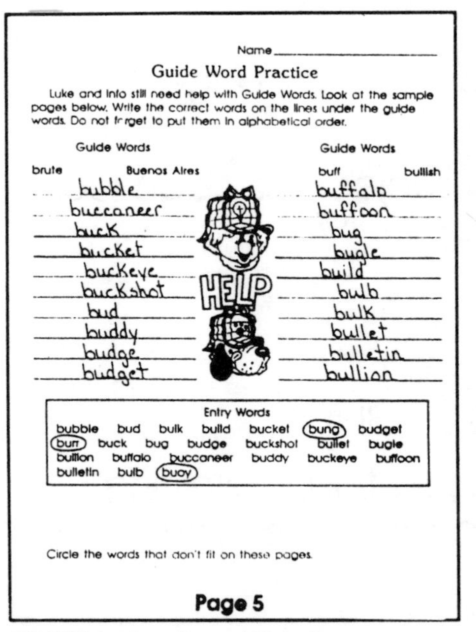

Name ____________

Guide Word Practice

Luke and Info still need help with Guide Words. Look at the sample pages below. Write the correct words on the lines under the guide words. Do not forget to put them in alphabetical order.

Guide Words: brute - Buenos Aires	Guide Words: buff - bullish
bubble	buffalo
buccaneer	buffoon
buck	bug
bucket	bugle
buckeye	build
buckshot	bulb
bud	bulk
buddy	bullet
budge	bulletin
budget	bullion

Entry Words

bubble bud bulk build bucket (bung) budget (burr) buck bug budge buckshot bullet bugle bullion buffalo buccaneer buddy buckeye buffoon bulletin bulb (buoy)

Circle the words that don't fit on these pages.

Page 5

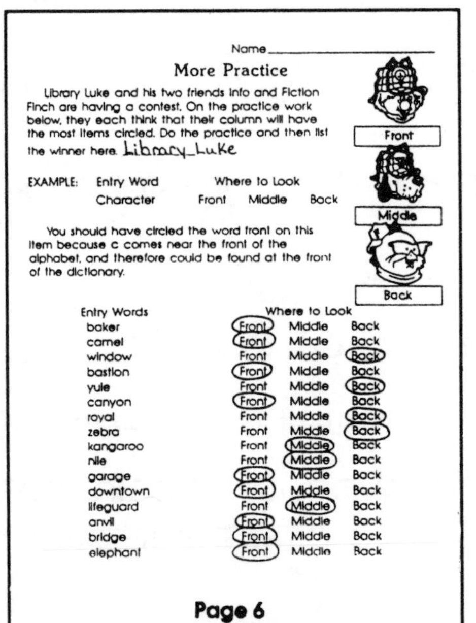

Name ____________

More Practice

Library Luke and his two friends Info and Fiction Finch are having a contest. On the practice work below, they each think that their column will have the most items circled. Do the practice and then list the winner here. Library Luke

EXAMPLE: Entry Word: Character; Where to Look: Front Middle Back

You should have circled the word front on this item because c comes near the front of the alphabet, and therefore could be found at the front of the dictionary.

Entry Words	Where to Look
baker	(Front) Middle Back
camel	(Front) Middle Back
window	Front Middle (Back)
bastion	(Front) Middle Back
yule	Front Middle (Back)
canyon	(Front) Middle Back
royal	Front Middle (Back)
zebra	Front Middle (Back)
kangaroo	Front (Middle) Back
nile	Front (Middle) Back
garage	(Front) Middle Back
downtown	(Front) Middle Back
lifeguard	Front (Middle) Back
anvil	(Front) Middle Back
bridge	(Front) Middle Back
elephant	(Front) Middle Back

Page 6

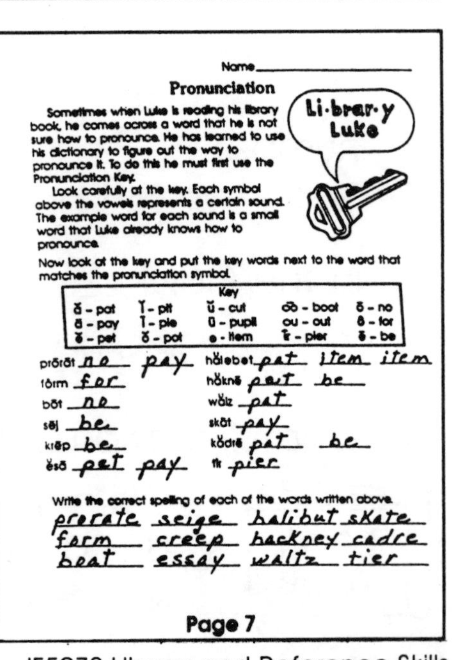

Name ____________

Pronunciation

Sometimes when Luke is reading his library book, he comes across a word that he is not sure how to pronounce. He has learned to use his dictionary to figure out the way to pronounce it. To do this he must first use the Pronunciation Key.

Look carefully at the key. Each symbol above the vowels represents a certain sound. The example word for each sound is a small word that Luke already knows how to pronounce.

Now look at the key and put the key words next to the word that matches the pronunciation symbol.

Key

ă - pat	ĭ - pit	ŭ - cut	ŏŏ - book	ō - no
ā - pay	ī - pie	ū - pupil	ou - out	ô - for
ĕ - pet	ŏ - pot	ə - item	îr - pier	ē - be

prōrāt no pay	hălebet pat item item
fôrm for	hăknē pat be
bōt no	wôlz pat
sēj be	skāt pay
krēp be	kădrē pat be
ĕsā pet pay	tîr pier

Write the correct spelling of each of the words written above.

prorate seige halibut skate
form creep hackney cadre
boat essay waltz tier

Page 7

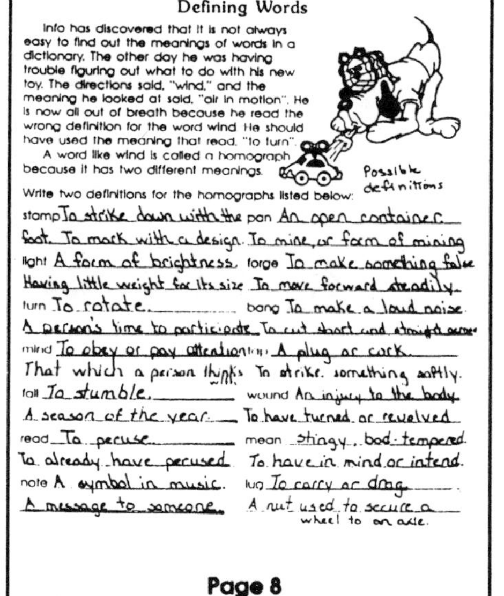

Name ______

Defining Words

Info has discovered that it is not always easy to find out the meanings of words in a dictionary. The other day he was having trouble figuring out what to do with his new toy. The directions said, "wind," and the meaning he looked at said, "air in motion". He is now all out of breath because he read the wrong definition for the word wind. He should have used the meaning that read, "to turn".

A word like wind is called a homograph because it has two different meanings.

Possible definitions

Write two definitions for the homographs listed below:

stamp To strike down with the foot. To mark with a design. — pan An open container. To mine, or form of mining
light A form of brightness. Having little weight for its size — forge To make something false. To move forward steadily.
turn To rotate. A person's time to participate. — bang To make a loud noise. To cut short and straight across
mind To obey or pay attention to. That which a person thinks — tip A plug or cork. To strike something softly.
fall To stumble. A season of the year. — wound An injury to the body. To have turned or revolved
read To peruse. To already have perused — mean Stingy, bad-tempered. To have in mind or intend.
note A symbol in music. A message to someone. — lug To carry or drag. A nut used to secure a wheel to an axle.

Page 8

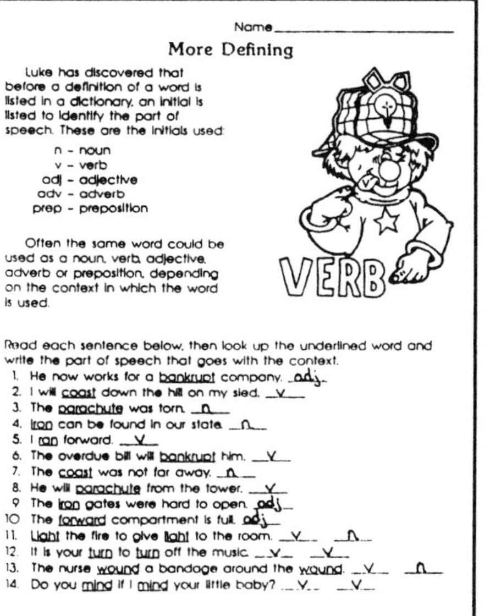

Name ______

More Defining

Luke has discovered that before a definition of a word is listed in a dictionary, an initial is listed to identify the part of speech. These are the initials used:

n - noun
v - verb
adj - adjective
adv - adverb
prep - preposition

Often the same word could be used as a noun, verb, adjective, adverb or preposition, depending on the context in which the word is used.

Read each sentence below, then look up the underlined word and write the part of speech that goes with the context.

1. He now works for a bankrupt company. adj.
2. I will coast down the hill on my sled. v
3. The parachute was torn. n
4. Iron can be found in our state. n
5. I ran forward. v
6. The overdue bill will bankrupt him. v
7. The coast was not far away. n
8. He will parachute from the tower. v
9. The iron gates were hard to open. adj.
10. The forward compartment is full. adj.
11. Light the fire to give light to the room. v n
12. It is your turn to turn off the music. n v
13. The nurse wound a bandage around the wound. v n
14. Do you mind if I mind your little baby? v v

Page 9

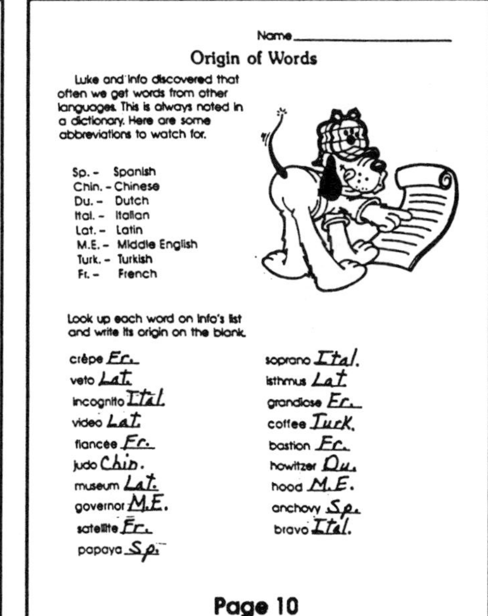

Name ______

Origin of Words

Luke and Info discovered that often we get words from other languages. This is always noted in a dictionary. Here are some abbreviations to watch for.

Sp. - Spanish
Chin. - Chinese
Du. - Dutch
Ital. - Italian
Lat. - Latin
M.E. - Middle English
Turk. - Turkish
Fr. - French

Look up each word on Info's list and write its origin on the blank.

crêpe Fr.	soprano Ital.
veto Lat.	isthmus Lat.
incognito Ital.	grandiose Fr.
video Lat.	coffee Turk.
fiancee Fr.	bastion Fr.
judo Chin.	howitzer Du.
museum Lat.	hood M.E.
governor M.E.	anchovy Sp.
satellite Fr.	bravo Ital.
papaya Sp.	

Page 10

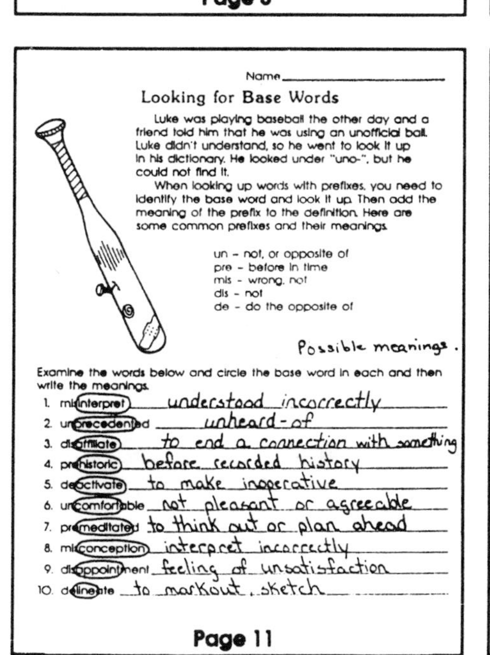

Name ______

Looking for Base Words

Luke was playing baseball the other day and a friend told him that he was using an unofficial ball. Luke didn't understand, so he went to look it up in his dictionary. He looked under "uno-", but he could not find it.

When looking up words with prefixes, you need to identify the base word and look it up. Then add the meaning of the prefix to the definition. Here are some common prefixes and their meanings.

un - not, or opposite of
pre - before in time
mis - wrong, not
dis - not
de - do the opposite of

Possible meanings.

Examine the words below and circle the base word in each and then write the meanings.

1. misinterpret understood incorrectly
2. unprecedented unheard-of
3. disaffiliate to end a connection with something
4. prehistoric before recorded history
5. deactivate to make inoperative
6. uncomfortable not pleasant or agreeable
7. premeditate to think out or plan ahead
8. misconception interpret incorrectly
9. disappointment feeling of unsatisfaction
10. delineate to markout, sketch

Page 11

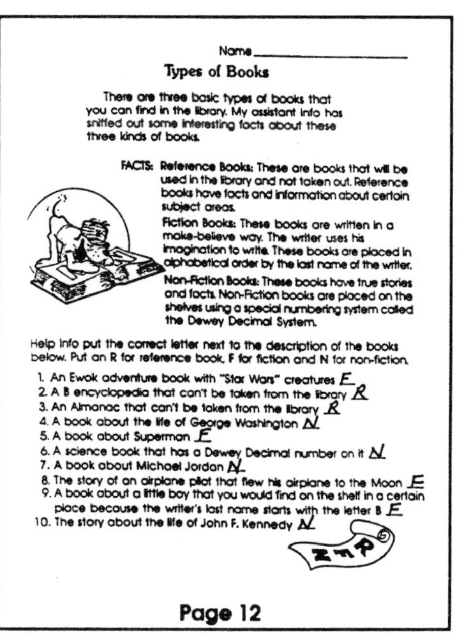

Name ______

Types of Books

There are three basic types of books that you can find in the library. My assistant Info has sniffed out some interesting facts about these three kinds of books.

FACTS: Reference Books: These are books that will be used in the library and not taken out. Reference books have facts and information about certain subject areas.

Fiction Books: These books are written in a make-believe way. The writer uses his imagination to write. These books are placed in alphabetical order by the last name of the writer.

Non-Fiction Books: These books have true stories and facts. Non-Fiction books are placed on the shelves using a special numbering system called the Dewey Decimal System.

Help Info put the correct letter next to the description of the books below. Put an R for reference book, F for fiction and N for non-fiction.

1. An Ewok adventure book with "Star Wars" creatures F
2. A B encyclopedia that can't be taken from the library R
3. An Almanac that can't be taken from the library R
4. A book about the life of George Washington N
5. A book about Superman F
6. A science book that has a Dewey Decimal number on it N
7. A book about Michael Jordan N
8. The story of an airplane pilot that flew his airplane to the Moon F
9. A book about a little boy that you would find on the shelf in a certain place because the writer's last name starts with the letter B F
10. The story about the life of John F. Kennedy N

Page 12

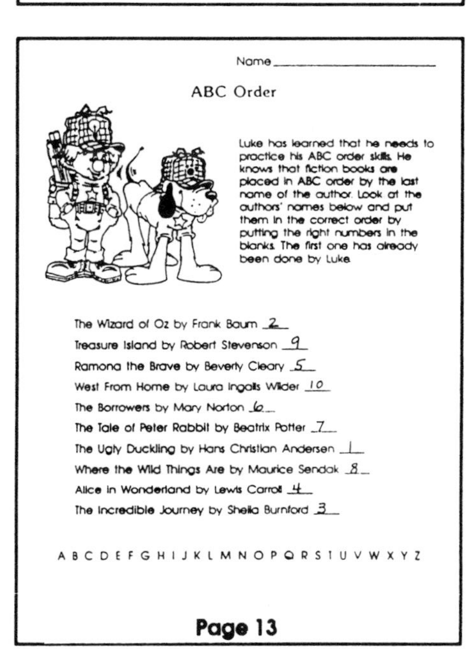

Name ______

ABC Order

Luke has learned that he needs to practice his ABC order skills. He knows that fiction books are placed in ABC order by the last name of the author. Look at the authors' names below and put them in the correct order by putting the right numbers in the blanks. The first one has already been done by Luke.

The Wizard of Oz by Frank Baum 2
Treasure Island by Robert Stevenson 9
Ramona the Brave by Beverly Cleary 5
West From Home by Laura Ingalls Wilder 10
The Borrowers by Mary Norton 6
The Tale of Peter Rabbit by Beatrix Potter 7
The Ugly Duckling by Hans Christian Andersen 1
Where the Wild Things Are by Maurice Sendak 8
Alice in Wonderland by Lewis Carroll 4
The Incredible Journey by Sheila Burnford 3

A B C D E F G H I J K L M N O P Q R S T U V W X Y Z

Page 13

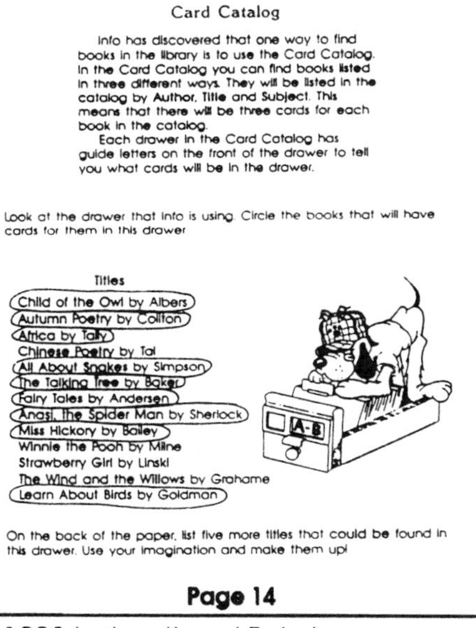

Name ______

Card Catalog

Info has discovered that one way to find books in the library is to use the Card Catalog. In the Card Catalog you can find books listed in three different ways. They will be listed in the catalog by Author, Title and Subject. This means that there will be three cards for each book in the catalog.

Each drawer in the Card Catalog has guide letters on the front of the drawer to tell you what cards will be in the drawer.

Look at the drawer that Info is using. Circle the books that will have cards for them in this drawer.

Titles

Child of the Owl by Albers
Autumn Poetry by Collton
Africa by Talty
Chinese Poetry by Tai
All About Snakes by Simpson
The Talking Tree by Baker
Fairy Tales by Andersen
Anasi, the Spider Man by Sherlock
Miss Hickory by Bailey
Winnie the Pooh by Milne
Strawberry Girl by Linski
The Wind and the Willows by Grahame
Learn About Birds by Goldman

On the back of the paper, list five more titles that could be found in this drawer. Use your imagination and make them up!

Page 14

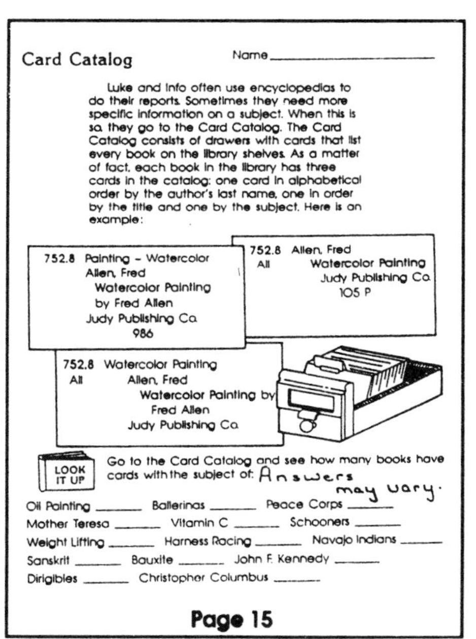

Card Catalog

Name ______

Luke and Info often use encyclopedias to do their reports. Sometimes they need more specific information on a subject. When this is so, they go to the Card Catalog. The Card Catalog consists of drawers with cards that list every book on the library shelves. As a matter of fact, each book in the library has three cards in the catalog: one card in alphabetical order by the author's last name, one in order by the title and one by the subject. Here is an example:

752.8 Painting - Watercolor
Allen, Fred
Watercolor Painting
by Fred Allen
Judy Publishing Co.
986

752.8 Allen, Fred
All Watercolor Painting
Judy Publishing Co.
105 P

752.8 Watercolor Painting
All Allen, Fred
Watercolor Painting by
Fred Allen
Judy Publishing Co.

LOOK IT UP — Go to the Card Catalog and see how many books have cards with the subject of: Answers may vary.

Oil Painting ______ Ballerinas ______ Peace Corps ______
Mother Teresa ______ Vitamin C ______ Schooners ______
Weight Lifting ______ Harness Racing ______ Navajo Indians ______
Sanskrit ______ Bauxite ______ John F. Kennedy ______
Dirigibles ______ Christopher Columbus ______

Page 15

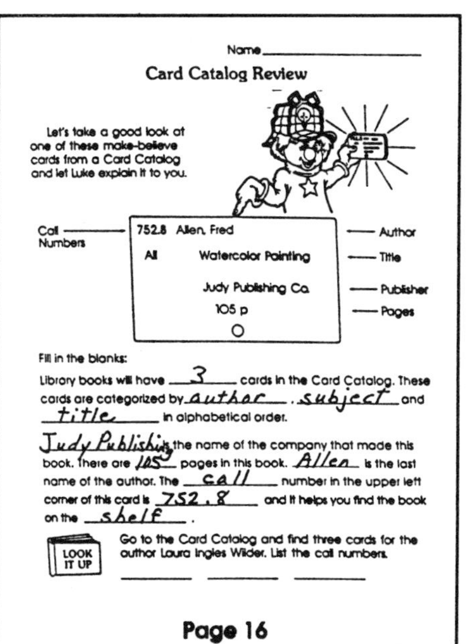

Name ______

Card Catalog Review

Let's take a good look at one of these make-believe cards from a Card Catalog and let Luke explain it to you.

Call Numbers — 752.8 All — Allen, Fred — Author
Watercolor Painting — Title
Judy Publishing Co. — Publisher
105 p — Pages

Fill in the blanks:

Library books will have 3 cards in the Card Catalog. These cards are categorized by author, subject and title in alphabetical order.

Judy Publishing the name of the company that made this book. There are 105 pages in this book. Allen is the last name of the author. The call number in the upper left corner of this card is 752.8 and it helps you find the book on the shelf.

LOOK IT UP — Go to the Card Catalog and find three cards for the author Laura Ingles Wilder. List the call numbers.

______ ______ ______

Page 16

Name ____________

Almanac

THE KNOW-IT-ALL-MANAC

Another reference book that Luke and Info have learned to appreciate is the Almanac. This is a book that contains lots of different kinds of facts and information. The facts and information is always very current because it is published each year.

The information is not listed in alphabetical order, so therefore you must always look in the index to find which page you need.

Use an Almanac to find the information called for below.

1. What is the current population of your state? ____________
2. In 1984, what were two important stories in the news? ____________
3. What is the governor's name in Colorado? Richard D. Lamm
4. What does Colorado mean? "red color"
5. Who won the Super Bowl this year? ____________
6. What motion picture won the Academy Award for best picture in 1984? "Amadeus"
7. Who are two people in the Baseball Hall of Fame? ____________
8. Who was Miss America in 1980? Cheryl Prewitt
9. What is the longest-running Broadway play ever? "A Chorus Line"
10. Who ran for U.S. President as an independent in the 1980 election? John Anderson

LOOK IT UP: List four interesting facts that you find in the 1985 almanac.

Page 17

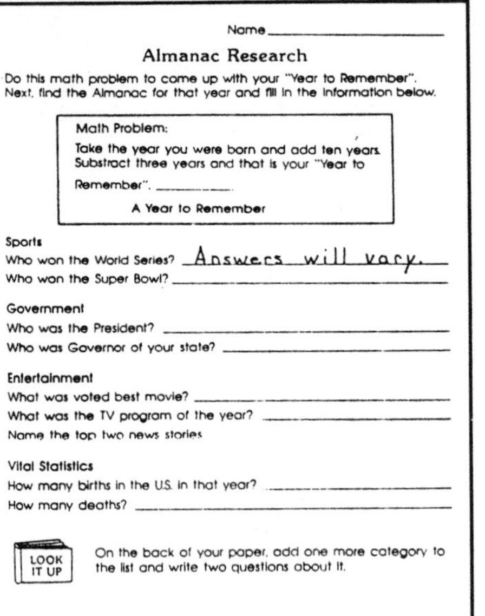
Name ____________

Almanac Research

Do this math problem to come up with your "Year to Remember". Next, find the Almanac for that year and fill in the information below.

Math Problem: Take the year you were born and add ten years. Substract three years and that is your "Year to Remember". ____ A Year to Remember

Sports
Who won the World Series? Answers will vary.
Who won the Super Bowl? ____________

Government
Who was the President? ____________
Who was Governor of your state? ____________

Entertainment
Who was voted best movie? ____________
What was the TV program of the year? ____________
Name the top two news stories ____________

Vital Statistics
How many births in the U.S. in that year? ____________
How many deaths? ____________

LOOK IT UP: On the back of your paper, add one more category to the list and write two questions about it.

Page 18

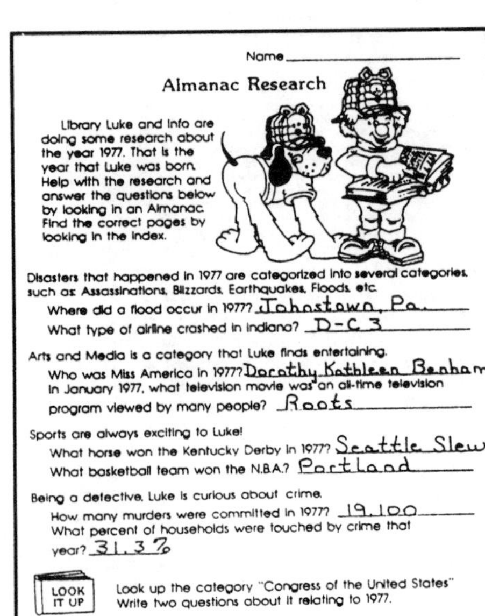
Name ____________

Almanac Research

Library Luke and Info are doing some research about the year 1977. That is the year that Luke was born. Help with the research and answer the questions below by looking in an Almanac. Find the correct pages by looking in the index.

Disasters that happened in 1977 are categorized into several categories, such as: Assassinations, Blizzards, Earthquakes, Floods, etc.
Where did a flood occur in 1977? Johnstown, Pa.
What type of airline crashed in Indiana? D-C 3

Arts and Media is a category that Luke finds entertaining.
Who was Miss America in 1977? Dorothy Kathleen Benham
In January 1977, what television movie was an all-time television program viewed by many people? Roots

Sports are always exciting to Luke!
What horse won the Kentucky Derby in 1977? Seattle Slew
What basketball team won the N.B.A.? Portland

Being a detective, Luke is curious about crime.
How many murders were committed in 1977? 19,100
What percent of households were touched by crime that year? 31.3%

LOOK IT UP: Look up the category "Congress of the United States". Write two questions about it relating to 1977.

Page 19

Name ____________

Atlas

Library Luke and Info have found another important research tool. It is called an Atlas. An Atlas is a book of maps.

Luke's parents are taking him on vacation soon. He promised his dad that he would learn to read a map so that he could help with directions.

They are going to Springfield, Illinois. On the map next to the name of the city, he found the code H-5. The H represents the letters along the side of the map. The number represents the numbers along the bottom of the map. This helps you find things on the map more easily.

Quincy, Beardstown, Jacksonville, Springfield, Chatham, Waverly, Pittsville, White Hall, Carlinville, Hillsboro, Granite City, Missouri, Illinois

Write the correct codes next to each city listed below.

Jacksonville H-3	Carlinville J-4	Pittsville I-2
Beardstown H-3	Quincy H-1	Chatham I-4
White Hall I-3	Waverly I-4	Granite City K-3
	Hillsboro J-4	

Library Luke lives in Quincy. What highway(s) would he take to get to Springfield? 24, 67, 125

Page 20

Name ____________

Introduction

While traveling in their time machine, Library Luke and his trusty dog, Info, landed in the middle of a library in the year 1876. A librarian named Melville Dewey was busy trying to sort the books into categories. He decided to sort the books into ten categories. Luke helped him. They gave each category a range of numbers. Here are the categories and their numbers. Another name for category is class name.

Categories	Numbers	List one book for each.
Generalities	000-099	Answers will vary.
Philosophy	100-199	
Religion	200-299	
Social Science	300-399	
Language	400-499	
Pure Science	500-599	
Technology	600-699	
Arts	700-799	
Literature	800-899	
Geography and History	900-999	

Unscramble these words to discover the name of the system Mr. Dewey invented.

EWYED MALDECI MESYTS

Dewey Decimal System

Page 21

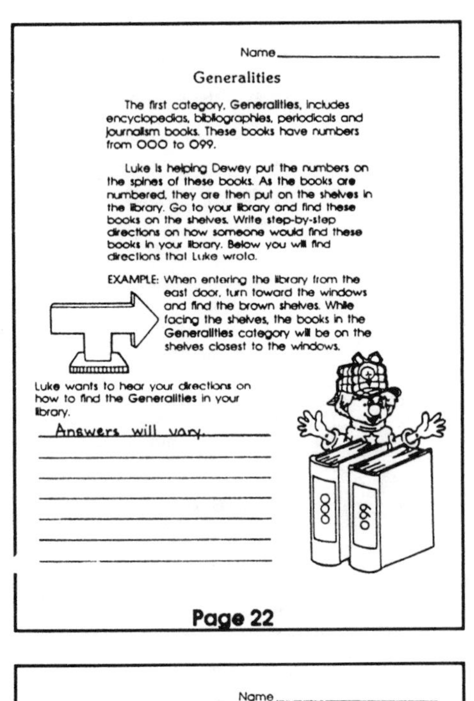
Name ____________

Generalities

The first category, Generalities, includes encyclopedias, bibliographies, periodicals and journalism books. These books have numbers from 000 to 099.

Luke is helping Dewey put the numbers on the spines of these books. As the books are numbered, they are then put on the shelves in the library. Go to your library and find these books on the shelves. Write step-by-step directions on how someone would find these books in your library. Below you will find directions that Luke wrote.

EXAMPLE: When entering the library from the east door, turn toward the windows and find the brown shelves. While facing the shelves, the books in the Generalities category will be on the shelves closest to the windows.

Luke wants to hear your directions on how to find the Generalities in your library.

Answers will vary.

Page 22

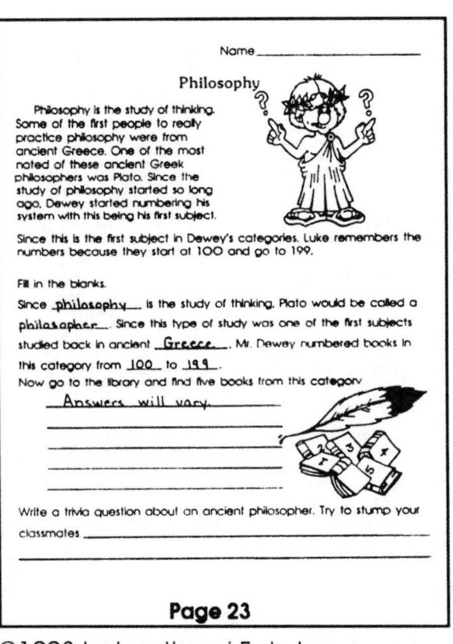
Name ____________

Philosophy

Philosophy is the study of thinking. Some of the first people to really practice philosophy were from ancient Greece. One of the most noted of these ancient Greek philosophers was Plato. Since the study of philosophy started so long ago, Dewey started numbering his system with this being his first subject.

Since this is the first subject in Dewey's categories, Luke remembers the numbers because they start at 100 and go to 199.

Fill in the blanks.

Since philosophy is the study of thinking, Plato would be called a philosopher. Since this type of study was one of the first subjects studied back in ancient Greece, Mr. Dewey numbered books in this category from 100 to 199.

Now go to the library and find five books from this category.

Answers will vary.

Write a trivia question about an ancient philosopher. Try to stump your classmates. ____________

Page 23

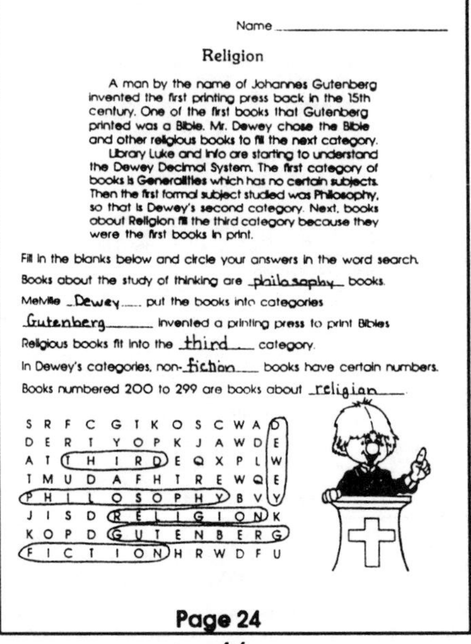
Name ____________

Religion

A man by the name of Johannes Gutenberg invented the first printing press back in the 15th century. One of the first books that Gutenberg printed was a Bible. Mr. Dewey chose the Bible and other religious books to fill the next category.

Library Luke and Info are starting to understand the Dewey Decimal System. The first category of books is Generalities which has no certain subjects. Then the first formal subject studied was Philosophy, so that is Dewey's second category. Next, books about Religion fill the third category because they were the first books in print.

Fill in the blanks below and circle your answers in the word search.

Books about the study of thinking are philosophy books.
Melville Dewey put the books into categories.
Gutenberg invented a printing press to print Bibles.
Religious books fit into the third category.
In Dewey's categories, non-fiction books have certain numbers.
Books numbered 200 to 299 are books about religion.

```
S R F C G T K O S C W A D
D E R T Y O P K J A W D E
A T T H I R D E Q X P L W
T M U D A F H T R E W Q E
P H I L O S O P H Y B V Y
J I S D R E L I G I O N K
K O P D G U T E N B E R G
F I C T I O N H R W D F U
```

Page 24

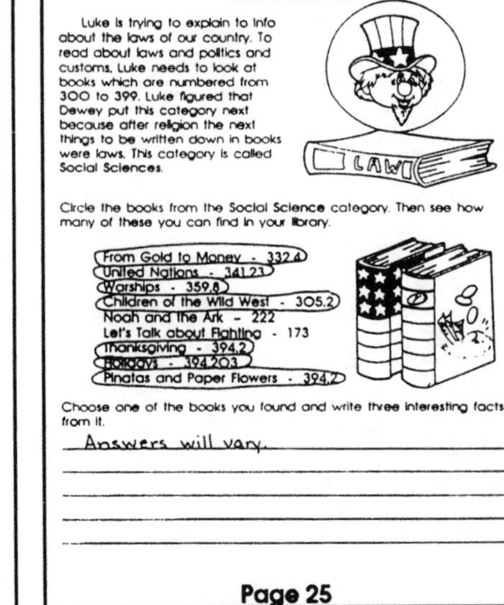
Name ____________

Social Science

Luke is trying to explain to Info about the laws of our country. To read about laws and politics and customs, Luke needs to look at books which are numbered from 300 to 399. Luke figured that Dewey put this category next because after religion the next things to be written down in books were laws. This category is called Social Sciences.

Circle the books from the Social Science category. Then see how many of these you can find in your library.

- From Gold to Money - 332.4 (circled)
- United Nations - 341.23 (circled)
- Worships - 359.8 (circled)
- Children of the Wild West - 305.2 (circled)
- Noah and the Ark - 222
- Let's Talk about Fighting - 173
- Thanksgiving - 394.2 (circled)
- Holidays - 394.203 (circled)
- Pinatas and Paper Flowers - 394.2 (circled)

Choose one of the books you found and write three interesting facts from it.

Answers will vary.

Page 25

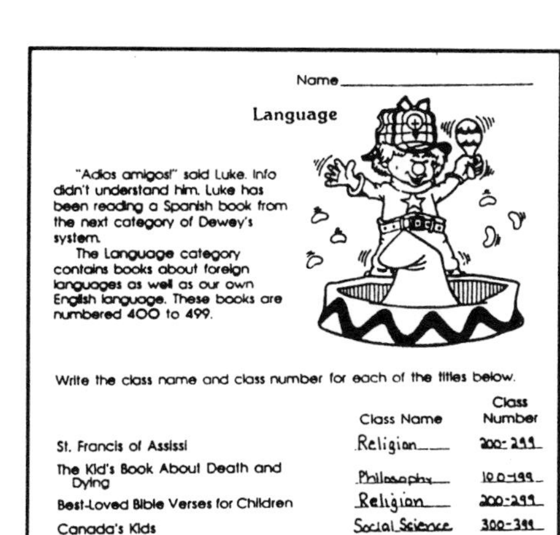

Name ____________

Language

"Adios amigos!" said Luke. Info didn't understand him. Luke has been reading a Spanish book from the next category of Dewey's system.

The Language category contains books about foreign languages as well as our own English language. These books are numbered 400 to 499.

Write the class name and class number for each of the titles below.

	Class Name	Class Number
St. Francis of Assissi	Religion	200-299
The Kid's Book About Death and Dying	Philosophy	100-199
Best-Loved Bible Verses for Children	Religion	200-299
Canada's Kids	Social Science	300-399
The Unions	Social Science	300-399
Christmas Time	Religion or Social Science	200-299 300-399
The Story of the Erie Canal	Social Science	300-399
Words to Talk About	Language	400-499
Language	Language	400-499

Page 26

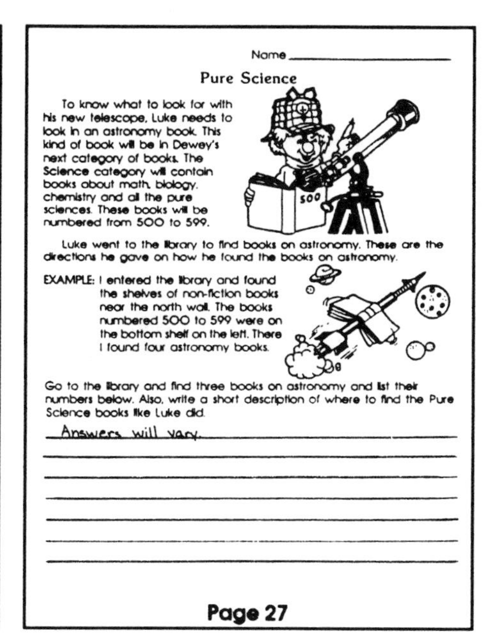

Name ____________

Pure Science

To know what to look for with his new telescope, Luke needs to look in an astronomy book. This kind of book will be in Dewey's next category of books. The Science category will contain books about math, biology, chemistry and all the pure sciences. These books will be numbered from 500 to 599.

Luke went to the library to find books on astronomy. These are the directions he gave on how he found the books on astronomy.

EXAMPLE: I entered the library and found the shelves of non-fiction books near the north wall. The books numbered 500 to 599 were on the bottom shelf on the left. There I found four astronomy books.

Go to the library and find three books on astronomy and list their numbers below. Also, write a short description of where to find the Pure Science books like Luke did.

Answers will vary.

Page 27

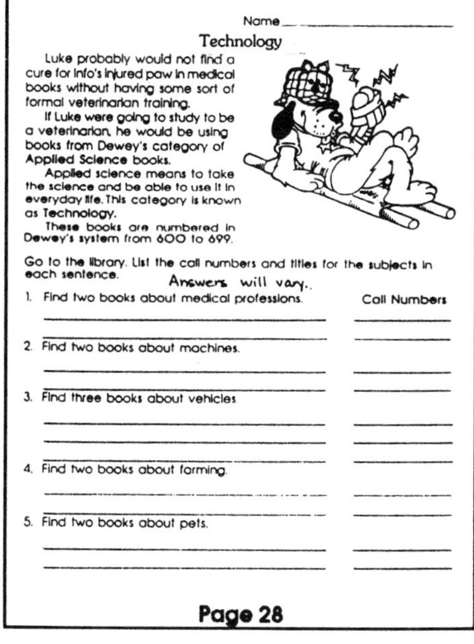

Name ____________

Technology

Luke probably would not find a cure for Info's injured paw in medical books without having some sort of formal veterinarian training.

If Luke were going to study to be a veterinarian, he would be using books from Dewey's category of Applied Science books.

Applied science means to take the science and be able to use it in everyday life. This category is known as Technology.

These books are numbered in Dewey's system from 600 to 699.

Go to the library. List the call numbers and titles for the subjects in each sentence. Answers will vary.

	Call Numbers
1. Find two books about medical professions.	
2. Find two books about machines.	
3. Find three books about vehicles	
4. Find two books about farming.	
5. Find two books about pets.	

Page 28

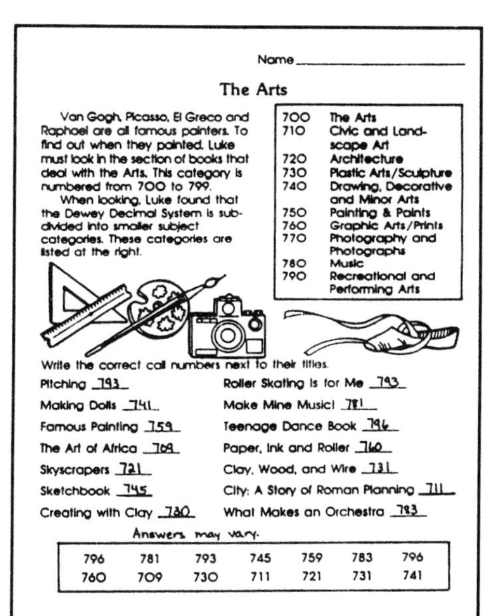

Name ____________

The Arts

Van Gogh, Picasso, El Greco and Raphael are all famous painters. To find out when they painted, Luke must look in the section of books that deal with the Arts. This category is numbered from 700 to 799.

When looking, Luke found that the Dewey Decimal System is subdivided into smaller subject categories. These categories are listed at the right.

700	The Arts
710	Civic and Landscape Art
720	Architecture
730	Plastic Arts/Sculpture
740	Drawing, Decorative and Minor Arts
750	Painting & Paints
760	Graphic Arts/Prints
770	Photography and Photographs
780	Music
790	Recreational and Performing Arts

Write the correct call numbers next to their titles.

Pitching 793	Roller Skating Is for Me 793
Making Dolls 741	Make Mine Music! 781
Famous Painting 759	Teenage Dance Book 796
The Art of Africa 709	Paper, Ink and Roller 760
Skyscrapers 721	Clay, Wood, and Wire 731
Sketchbook 745	City: A Story of Roman Planning 711
Creating with Clay 730	What Makes an Orchestra 783

Answers may vary.

796	781	793	745	759	783	796
760	709	730	711	721	731	741

Page 29

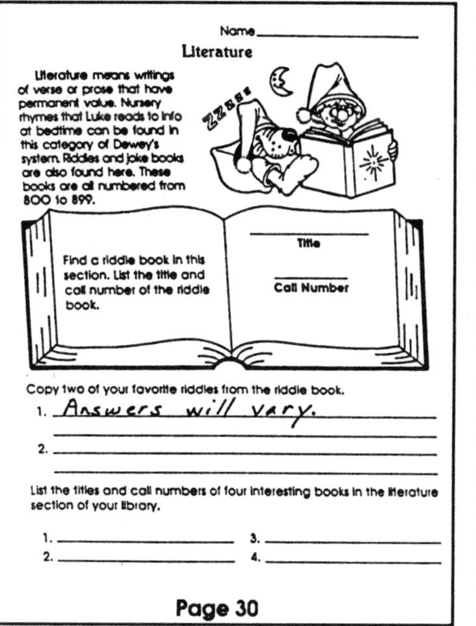

Name ____________

Literature

Literature means writings of verse or prose that have permanent value. Nursery rhymes that Luke reads to Info at bedtime can be found in this category of Dewey's system. Riddles and joke books are also found here. These books are all numbered from 800 to 899.

Find a riddle book in this section. List the title and call number of the riddle book.

Title ____________

Call Number ____________

Copy two of your favorite riddles from the riddle book.

1. Answers will vary.
2. ____________

List the titles and call numbers of four interesting books in the literature section of your library.

1. ____________ 3. ____________
2. ____________ 4. ____________

Page 30

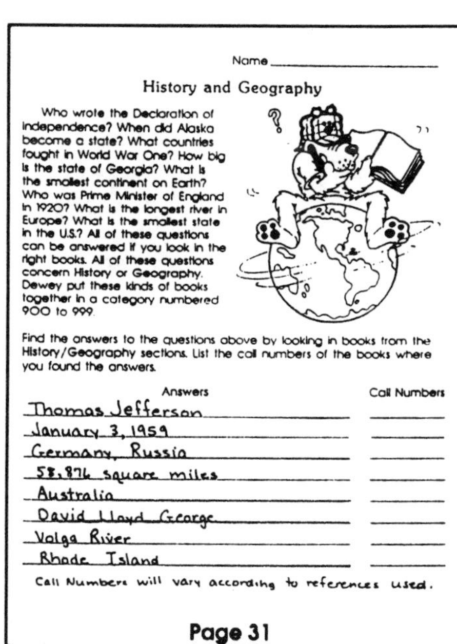

Name ____________

History and Geography

Who wrote the Declaration of Independence? When did Alaska become a state? What countries fought in World War One? How big is the state of Georgia? What is the smallest continent on Earth? Who was Prime Minister of England in 1920? What is the longest river in Europe? What is the smallest state in the U.S.? All of these questions can be answered if you look in the right books. All of these questions concern History or Geography. Dewey put these kinds of books together in a category numbered 900 to 999.

Find the answers to the questions above by looking in books from the History/Geography sections. List the call numbers of the books where you found the answers.

Answers	Call Numbers
Thomas Jefferson	
January 3, 1959	
Germany, Russia	
58,876 square miles	
Australia	
David Lloyd George	
Volga River	
Rhode Island	

Call Numbers will vary according to references used.

Page 31

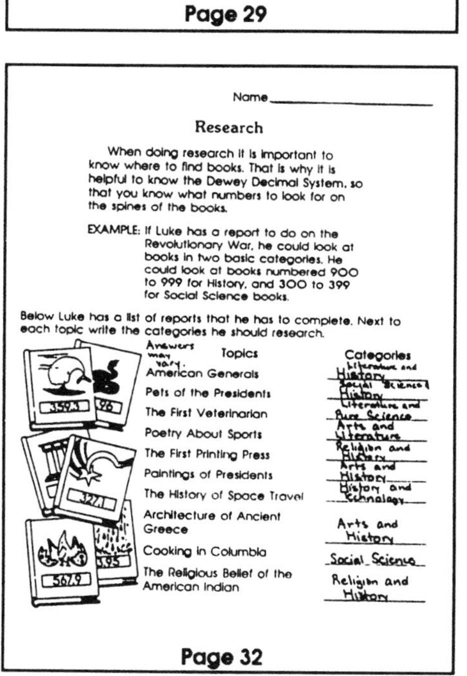

Name ____________

Research

When doing research it is important to know where to find books. That is why it is helpful to know the Dewey Decimal System, so that you know what numbers to look for on the spines of the books.

EXAMPLE: If Luke has a report to do on the Revolutionary War, he could look at books in two basic categories. He could look at books numbered 900 to 999 for History, and 300 to 399 for Social Science books.

Below Luke has a list of reports that he has to complete. Next to each topic write the categories he should research.

Answers may vary.

Topics	Categories
American Generals	Literature and History
Pets of the Presidents	Social Science and History
The First Veterinarian	Literature and Pure Science
Poetry About Sports	Arts and Literature
The First Printing Press	Religion and History
Paintings of Presidents	Arts and History
The History of Space Travel	History and Technology
Architecture of Ancient Greece	Arts and History
Cooking in Columbia	Social Science
The Religious Belief of the American Indian	Religion and History

Page 32

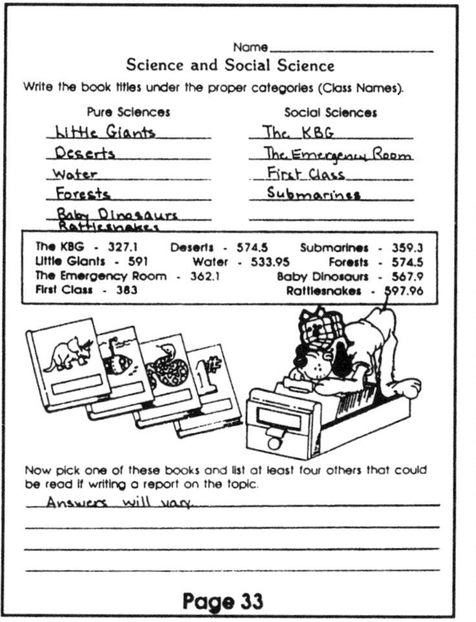

Name ____________

Science and Social Science

Write the book titles under the proper categories (Class Names).

Pure Sciences	Social Sciences
Little Giants	The KBG
Deserts	The Emergency Room
Water	First Class
Forests	Submarines
Baby Dinosaurs	
Rattlesnakes	

The KBG - 327.1	Deserts - 574.5	Submarines - 359.3
Little Giants - 591	Water - 533.95	Forests - 574.5
The Emergency Room - 362.1		Baby Dinosaurs - 567.9
First Class - 383		Rattlesnakes - 597.96

Now pick one of these books and list at least four others that could be read if writing a report on the topic.

Answers will vary.

Page 33

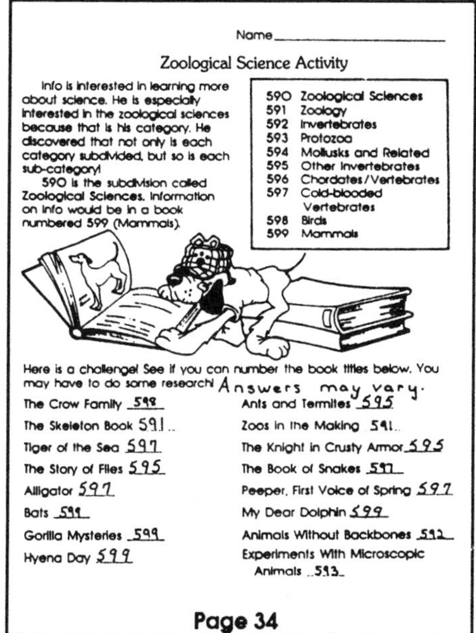

Name ____________

Zoological Science Activity

Info is interested in learning more about science. He is especially interested in the zoological sciences because that is his category. He discovered that not only is each category subdivided, but so is each sub-category!

590 is the subdivision called Zoological Sciences. Information on Info would be in a book numbered 599 (Mammals).

590	Zoological Sciences
591	Zoology
592	Invertebrates
593	Protozoa
594	Mollusks and Related
595	Other Invertebrates
596	Chordates/Vertebrates
597	Cold-blooded Vertebrates
598	Birds
599	Mammals

Here is a challenge! See if you can number the book titles below. You may have to do some research! Answers may vary.

The Crow Family 598	Ants and Termites 595
The Skeleton Book 591	Zoos in the Making 591
Tiger of the Sea 597	The Knight in Crusty Armor 595
The Story of Flies 595	The Book of Snakes 597
Alligator 597	Peeper, First Voice of Spring 597
Bats 599	My Dear Dolphin 599
Gorilla Mysteries 599	Animals Without Backbones 592
Hyena Day 599	Experiments With Microscopic Animals 593

Page 34

Name ____________

Encyclopedias

Luke is climbing into an encyclopedia. If you have never climbed into one, Luke would like to invite you to climb into one soon.

An encyclopedia is set up in alphabetical order just like a dictionary. Anytime you have a question about anything, the encyclopedia is one of the first places you can look for an answer.

One of the neat things about encyclopedias is that if you look something up, you usually find out information that will lead you to look for something else in the encyclopedia.

Luke is going to look up airplanes in the A encyclopedia. When he looks it up, he will discover that the first airplane was invented by the Wright brothers. Can you guess which encyclopedia Luke will look in next to learn more about the Wright brothers?

Circle the correct encyclopedia.

List the encyclopedia you will need to answer these questions.

1. When did man first land on the moon? M
2. When was George Washington born? W
3. Who is Governor of Arizona? A
4. What is a baseball made of? B
5. How big is a football field? F
6. Where is Mt. Everest? M
7. Who lived at Monticello? M
8. Who invented the car? C

Page 35

Name ____________

Encyclopedias

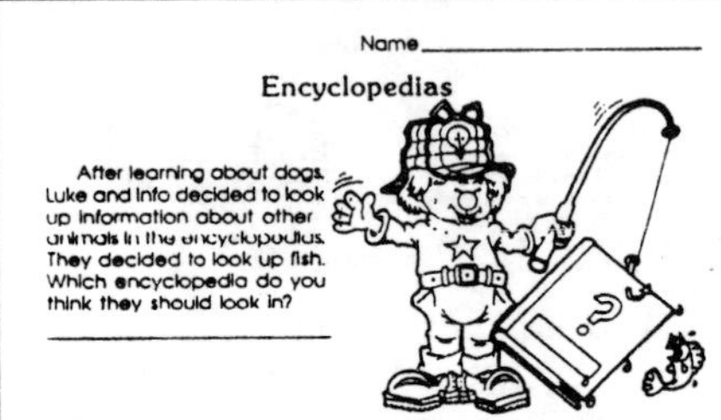

After learning about dogs, Luke and Info decided to look up information about other animals in the encyclopedias. They decided to look up fish. Which encyclopedia do you think they should look in?

Look up fish in your encyclopedia and answer the questions below.

1. Do fish have backbones? yes
2. Where would you find the smallest fish swimming? Phillippines
3. What is the largest fish in the ocean? whale shark
4. Name a fish that can fly. California flying fish
5. How do fish breathe under water? gills
6. How long are seahorses? 5 inches
7. What is the name of the fin on the side of a fish? pectoral
8. When did the first fish appear on the earth? 500 million years ago.
9. Name a fish that you find unusual looking. Answers will vary.
10. Name a fish with more than two colors. Answers will vary.

This is enough information to write a report on fish. Write one using these facts. But don't just copy out of the encyclopedia!

Page 36

Name ____________

Encyclopedias

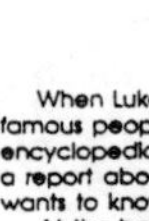

When Luke wants to find information about famous people, he often looks in the encyclopedia first. Especially when he is doing a report about a famous person. He usually wants to know when the person was born.

At the beginning of an article about a famous person, you will find something that looks like this: (1952-1978). The first date in parenthesis, 1952, tells when the person was born. The second date refers to when the person died. Luke's would look like this if he were in the encyclopedia: (1977 -). This means that Luke was born in 1977, but that he has not died yet.

Go to the library and find the articles about these famous people. Fill in the correct dates in parenthesis for each individual.

John F. Kennedy	(1917-1963)	Ian Fleming	(1908-1964)
Thomas Edison	(1847-1931)	Gertrude Ederle	(1906-)
Jackie Robinson	(1919-1972)	Walt Disney	(1901-1966)
Ronald Reagan	(1911-)	William Bonney	(1859-1881)
Judy Garland	(1922-1969)	Patrick Henry	(1736-1799)
Susan B. Anthony	(1820-1906)	Herbert Hoover	(1874-1964)
Daniel Boone	(1734-1820)	W. C. Fields	(1880-1946)
Mary Bethune	(1875-1955)	Eli Whitney	(1765-1825)
Elizabeth Browning	(1806-1861)	Babe Ruth	(1895-1948)
Abe Lincoln	(1809-1865)	Humphrey Bogart	(1899-1957)

Write a short paragraph about one of these famous people.

Page 37

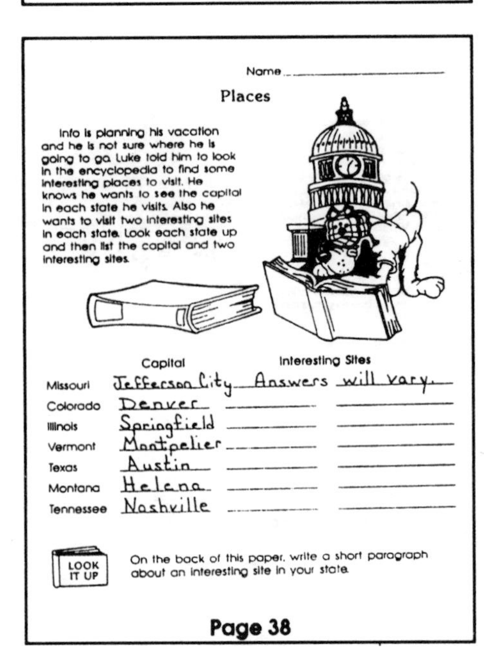

Name ____________

Places

Info is planning his vacation and he is not sure where he is going to go. Luke told him to look in the encyclopedia to find some interesting places to visit. He knows he wants to see the capital in each state he visits. Also he wants to visit two interesting sites in each state. Look each state up and then list the capital and two interesting sites.

	Capital	Interesting Sites	
Missouri	Jefferson City	Answers will vary.	
Colorado	Denver		
Illinois	Springfield		
Vermont	Montpelier		
Texas	Austin		
Montana	Helena		
Tennessee	Nashville		

LOOK IT UP — On the back of this paper, write a short paragraph about an interesting site in your state.

Page 38

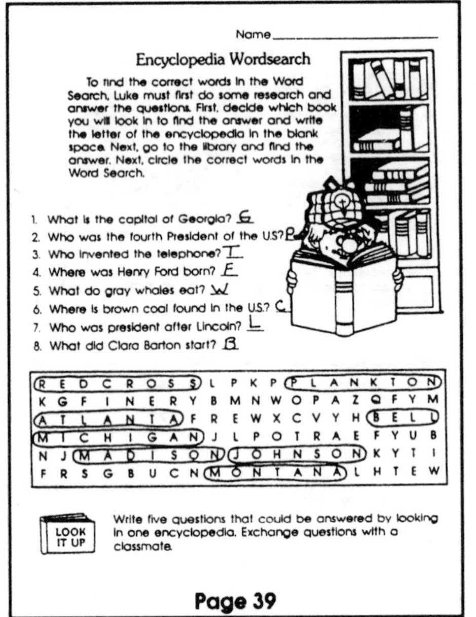

Name ____________

Encyclopedia Wordsearch

To find the correct words in the Word Search, Luke must first do some research and answer the questions. First, decide which book you will look in to find the answer and write the letter of the encyclopedia in the blank space. Next, go to the library and find the answer. Next, circle the correct words in the Word Search.

1. What is the capital of Georgia? G
2. Who was the fourth President of the U.S.? P
3. Who invented the telephone? T
4. Where was Henry Ford born? F
5. What do gray whales eat? W
6. Where is brown coal found in the U.S.? C
7. Who was president after Lincoln? L
8. What did Clara Barton start? B

```
R E D C R O S S L P K P P L A N K T O N
K G F I N E R Y B M N W O P A Z Q F Y M
A T L A N T A F R E W X C V Y H B E L L
M I C H I G A N J L P O T R A E F Y U B
N J M A D I S O N J O H N S O N K Y T I
F R S G B U C N M O N T A N A L H T E W
```

LOOK IT UP — Write five questions that could be answered by looking in one encyclopedia. Exchange questions with a classmate.

Page 39

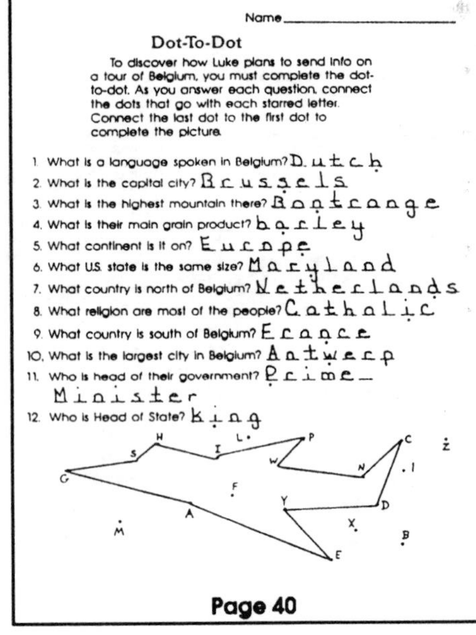

Name ____________

Dot-To-Dot

To discover how Luke plans to send info on a tour of Belgium, you must complete the dot-to-dot. As you answer each question, connect the dots that go with each starred letter. Connect the last dot to the first dot to complete the picture.

1. What is a language spoken in Belgium? Dutch
2. What is the capital city? Brussels
3. What is the highest mountain there? Botrange
4. What is their main grain product? barley
5. What continent is it on? Europe
6. What U.S. state is the same size? Maryland
7. What country is north of Belgium? Netherlands
8. What religion are most of the people? Catholic
9. What country is south of Belgium? France
10. What is the largest city in Belgium? Antwerp
11. Who is head of their government? Prime Minister
12. Who is Head of State? king

Page 40

Name ____________

Encyclopedia Research

DOWN

1. Andrew Jackson died in what city?
2. What is the capital of the state where Abe Lincoln was born?
3. The president who followed Lincoln was born in what city?

ACROSS

4. What is the main agricultural product in Kansas?
5. What is the state bird of Lincoln's birthplace?
6. What river is near President Franklin Roosevelt's birthplace?
7. Thomas Jefferson was born in what state?
8. What president followed Theodore Roosevelt?
9. What state became a state when Theodore Roosevelt was in office?
10. What is the smallest state in the U.S.?

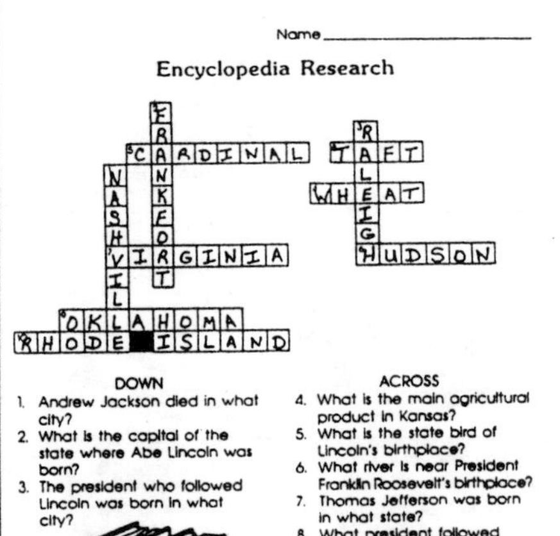

Answers: NASHVILLE, FRANKFORT, RALEIGH, WHEAT, CARDINAL, HUDSON, VIRGINIA, TAFT, OKLAHOMA, RHODE ISLAND

Page 41

Name ____________

Library Review

Poor Info is so tired. He is ready to rest and let you use the information you have learned about libraries to fill in these answers.

Use these words to fill in the blanks.

fiction biography non-fiction Dewey Caldecott

1. A book about a famous person's life is called a biography
2. The Caldecott Medal is an award given to special books.
3. "How to" books are called non-fiction
4. Dewey was a librarian who invented a system of placing books in order in a library.
5. A book that is make-believe is called fiction

Now write a T if the sentence is true and F if it is false.

6. Fiction books are put in alphabetical order by their author's last name. T
7. There are three kinds of books with Dewey Decimal numbers. F
8. Reference books are untrue. F
9. To find out about current things, look in an Almanac. T
10. We usually keep reference books in the library. T

Crossword Puzzle Fun

Across
1. Use a whisper voice while in the? library
3. Another word for writer is? author
5. What kind of number helps us find books? call

Down
2. You can find maps where? atlas
4. Ben Franklin's life story is a? biography

Page 42

Name ____________

Reference Review

Info made a terrible mistake. His paw accidently hit the board where Luke was doing his homework and got the answers to the questions all scrambled up. Your job is to unscramble the words and put the correct answers on the lines.

recurtn	exind	ilnolnc	eddi	raesherc
protser	lasat	olctaog	revorgon	lamacan

1. In the encyclopedia, you can find out when a famous person was born and died.
2. If you look up a state in the encyclopedia, you can discover the head of the government, the governor
3. The index is where all the subjects in an Almanac are listed by page numbers.
4. Encyclopedias are very helpful when doing reports.
5. To find out about Abe Lincoln's life, you should look up Lincoln.
6. Current events can be found in a yearly Almanac.
7. The almanac will be subjects listed in the index by page number.
8. To find all the books in a library on a certain subject, you can look in the Card catalog.
9. Maps of many places will be found in an atlas.
10. When information is gathered for a report, we call it research.

LOOK IT UP — Write five facts about Lincoln that you find interesting. Use at least two different reference books. List your sources.

Page 43